PENGUIN BOOKS

THE PENGUIN METAPHYSICAL LIBRARY
General Editor: Jacob Needleman

BOYHOOD WITH GURDJIEFF

Fritz Peters was born in Madison, Wisconsin, in 1913. Following his four years with Gurdjieff in France, he attended business school in the United States. He returned to Europe with the army during World War II, serving in England, France, Luxemburg, and Belgium. In the years since the war, his novels *The World Next Door*, *Finistère*, and *The Descent* have been widely read. He is also the author of short stories and of a children's book, *The Book of the Year*.

FRITZ PETERS

BOYHOOD
WITH
GURDJIEFF

PENGUIN BOOKS INC
Baltimore · Maryland

Penguin Books Inc
7110 Ambassador Road
Baltimore, Maryland 21207, U.S.A.

First published by E. P. Dutton & Co., Inc. 1964
Published in Penguin Books 1972
Reprinted 1973

Copyright © Fritz Peters, 1964

Printed in the United States of America by
Kingsport Press, Inc., Kingsport, Tennessee 37662

THE PENGUIN METAPHYSICAL LIBRARY

The Penguin Metaphysical Library is intended to serve the present need for living ideas — ideas that can move contemporary people to the struggle for self-knowledge. Unfortunately, by the very nature of today's crisis, most of us lack a touchstone by which to recognize ideas that can open us to see what is actually new and more alive.

The marvels of modern science are the result of a movement toward more liberal education and greater freedom of inquiry, which began long ago with the avowed purpose of widening human knowledge. As a result, however, man has thrust upon himself a standard of knowing and a view of reality which blind him to his possible role within the universal scheme. As the pressure of technology increases, authentic patterns of human life are more and more upset, and a descent into total materialism seems inevitable.

Fears of this descent have finally evoked a counterliterature about ancient psychology and esoteric teachings, largely of Oriental origin, which is supposed to reverse the current. Yet it may all be part of the same process. For most of us, the truly wide view of life will remain hidden between the lines. Even the wisdom of great masters, if it does not enter correctly into our minds, will only burden our already dull and awkward responses with added information.

Man remains, as at all times, an enigma — a "two-natured being," partly divine and partly an animal that reads. Are there special books in this flood of written material that can draw from us, as we read them, the sincerity to listen to the whole truth amid the din of rival forms and teachings and promises — books that both help us to awaken to the real meaning of living and bring us a good night's sleep?

In offering a selection from the many available texts, the editor has necessarily to rely on his own need and hunger for a more impartial sense of himself — a hunger that is far from being permanent or satisfied. His wish is that, at the least, The Penguin Metaphysical Library may help others to hear great ideas in a way that does not support the illusions that have generated the present confusion.

JACOB NEEDLEMAN

This book is dedicated to the memory of Georges Gurdjieff,
with an acknowledgment of a debt of thanks to:
Sheila Hodges
Lloyd L. Goff
Anne Raymond
and Julia B. Tappan
without whose interest and enthusiasm
it might never have been written.

Boyhood with GURDJIEFF

I

I MET AND talked to Georges Gurdjieff for the first time in 1924, on a Saturday afternoon in June, at the Château du Prieuré in Fontainebleau-Avon, France. Although the reasons for my being there were not very clear in my mind—I was eleven at the time—my memory of that meeting is still brilliantly clear.

It was a bright, sunny day. Gurdjieff was sitting by a small marble-topped table, shaded by a striped umbrella, with his back to the château proper, facing a large expanse of formal lawns and flower beds. I had to sit on the terrace of the château, behind him, for some time before I was summoned to his side for an interview. I had, actually, seen him once before, in New York the previous winter, but I did not feel that I had "met" him. My only memory of that prior time was that I had been frightened of him: partly because of the way he looked at —or through—me, and partly because of his reputation. I had been told that he was at least a "prophet"—at most, something very close to the "second coming of Christ".

Meeting any version of a "Christ" is an event, and this meeting was not one to which I looked forward. Facing the presence not only did not appeal to me—I dreaded it.

The actual meeting did not measure up to my fears. "Messiah" or not, he seemed to me a simple, straightforward man. He was not surrounded by any halo, and while his English was heavily accented, he spoke far more simply than the Bible had led me to expect. He made a vague gesture in my direction, told me to sit down, called for coffee, and then asked me why I was there. I was relieved to find that he seemed to be an ordinary human being, but I was troubled by the question. I felt sure that I was supposed to give him an *important* answer; that I should have some excellent reason. Having none, I told him the truth: That I was there because I had been brought there.

He then asked me why I wanted to be there, to study at his school. Once more I was only able to answer that it was all beyond my control—I had not been consulted, I had been, as it were, transported to that place. I remember my strong impulse to lie to him, and my equally strong feeling that I could not lie to him. I felt sure that he knew the truth in advance. The only question that I answered less than honestly was when he asked me if I wanted to stay there and to study with him. I said that I did, which was not essentially true. I said it because I knew that it was expected of me. It seems to me, now, that any child would have answered as I did. Whatever the Prieuré might represent to adults (and the literal name of the school was "The Gurdjieff Institute for the Harmonious Development of Man"), I felt that I was experiencing the equivalent of being interviewed by the principal of a high school. Children went to school, and I subscribed to the general agreement that no child would tell his teacher-to-be that he did not want to go to school. The only thing that surprised me was that I was asked the question.

Gurdjieff then asked me two more questions:

1. What do you think life is?

and

2. What do you want to know?

I answered the first question by saying: "I think life is something that is handed to you on a silver platter, and it is up to you (me) to do something with it." This answer touched off a long discussion about the phrase "on a silver platter", including a reference by Gurdjieff to the head of John the Baptist. I retreated—it felt like a retreat—and modified the phrase to the effect that life was a "gift", and this seemed to please him.

The second question (What do you want to know?) was simpler to answer. My words were: "I want to know everything."

Gurdjieff replied immediately: "You cannot know everything. Everything about what?"

I said: "Everything about man," and then added: "In English I think it is called psychology or maybe philosophy."

He sighed then, and after a short silence said: "You can stay. But your answer makes life difficult for me. I am the only one who teaches what you ask. You make more work for me."

Since my childish aims were to conform and to please, I was disconcerted by his answer. The last thing I wanted to do was to make life more difficult for anyone—it seemed to me that it was difficult enough already. I said nothing in reply to this, and he went on to tell me that in addition to learning "every-thing" I would also have the opportunity to study lesser subjects, such as languages, mathematics, various sciences, and so forth. He also said that I would find that his was not the usual school: "Can learn many things here that other schools not teach." He then patted my shoulder benevolently.

I use the word "benevolently" because the gesture was of great importance to me at the time. I longed for approval from some higher authority. To receive such "approval" from this man who was considered by other adults to be a "prophet", "seer", and/or a "Messiah"—and approval in such a simple, friendly gesture—was unexpected and heartwarming. I beamed.

His manner changed abruptly. He struck the table with one fist, looked at me with great intensity, and said: "Can you promise to do something for me?"

His voice and the look he had given me were frightening and also exciting. I felt both cornered and challenged. I answered him with one word, a firm "Yes".

He gestured towards the expanse of lawns before us: "You see this grass?"

"Yes."

"I give you work. You must cut this grass, with machine, every week."

I looked at the lawns, the grass spreading before us into what appeared to me infinity. It was, without any doubt, a prospect of more work in one week than I had ever contemplated in my life. Again, I said "Yes".

He struck the table with his fist for a second time. "You must promise on your God." His voice was deadly serious. "You must promise that you will do this thing no matter what happens."

I looked at him, questioning, respectful, and with considerable awe. No lawn—not even these (there were four of them)—had ever seemed important to me before. "I promise," I said earnestly.

"Not just promise," he reiterated. "Must promise you will do no matter what happens, no matter who try stop you. Many things can happen in life."

For a moment his words conjured up visions of terrifying arguments over the mowing of these lawns. I foresaw great emotional dramas taking place in the future on account of these lawns and of myself. Once again, I promised. I was as serious as he was then. I would have died, if necessary, in the act of mowing the lawns.

My feeling of dedication was obvious, and he seemed satisfied. He told me to begin work on Monday, and then dismissed me. I don't think I realized it at the time—that is, the sensation was new to me—but I left him with the feeling that I had fallen in love; whether with the man, the lawns, or myself, did not matter. My chest was expanded far beyond its normal capacity. I, a child, an unimportant cog in the world which belonged to adults, had been asked to perform something that was apparently vital.

II

WHAT WAS "THE PRIEURÉ", which was the name most of us used, or "The Institute for the Harmonious Development of Man"?

At the age of eleven, I understood it to be simply some kind of special school, directed, as I have said, by a man who was considered by many people to be a visionary, a new prophet, a great philosopher. Gurdjieff himself once defined it as a place where he was attempting, among other things, to create a small world that would reproduce the conditions of the larger, outside world; the main purpose in creating such conditions being to prepare the students for future human, or life, experience. It was not, in other words, a school devoted to ordinary education which, generally, consists in the acquisition of various faculties such as reading, writing, and arithmetic. One of the simpler things that he was attempting to teach was a preparation for life itself.

It may be necessary to point out here, especially for the benefit of people who have had some contact with Gurdjieffian theory, that I am describing the "Institute" as I saw and understood it as a boy. I am not attempting to define its purpose or meaning for individuals who were interested in, or attracted to, Gurdjieff because of his philosophy. To me, it was simply another school—different from any school I had known, to be sure—and the essential difference was that most of the "students" were adults. With the exception of my brother and myself, all the other children were either relatives—nieces, nephews, etc., of Mr. Gurdjieff—or his natural children. There were not many children in all: I can only remember a total of ten.

The routine of the school, for everyone except the smallest children, was the same. The day began with a breakfast of coffee and dry toast at six o'clock. From seven o'clock on, each individual worked at whatever task was assigned to him. The performance of these tasks was only interrupted during the day by meals: dinner at noon (usually, soup, meat, salad, and some kind of sweet pudding); tea at four in the afternoon; a simple supper at seven in the evening. After supper, at 8.30, there were gymnastics, or dances, in what was called the "study-house". This routine was standard for six days a week, except that on Saturday afternoons the women went to the Turkish bath; early Saturday evenings there were "demonstrations" of the dances in the study-house by the more competent performers, for the other students and for guests who frequently came to visit for weekends; after the demonstrations, the men went to the Turkish bath, and when the bath was over, there was a "feast" or special meal. The children did not participate in these late meals as diners—only as waiters or kitchen help. Sunday was a day of rest.

The tasks assigned to the students were invariably concerned with the actual functioning of the school: gardening, cooking, house-cleaning, taking care of animals, milking, making butter; and these tasks were almost always group activities. As I learned later, the group work was considered to be of real importance: Different personalities, working together, produced subjective, human conflicts; human conflicts produced friction; friction revealed characteristics which, if observed, could reveal "self". One of the many aims of the school was "to see yourself as others saw you"; to see oneself, as it were, from a distance; to be able to criticize that self objectively; but, at first, simply to *see* it. An exercise that was intended to be performed all the time, during whatever physical activity, was called "self-observation" or "opposing I to it"—"I" being the (potential) consciousness, "it" the body, the instrument.

At the beginning, and before I understood any of these theories or exercises, my task and, in a sense, my world, was completely centred on cutting the grass, for my lawns—as I came to call them—became considerably more vital than I could have anticipated.

The day after my "interview" with him, Mr. Gurdjieff left for Paris. We had been given to understand that it was customary for him to spend two days a week in Paris, usually accompanied by his secretary, Madame de Hartmann, and sometimes others. This time, which was unusual, he went alone.

As I remember, it was not until sometime on Monday afternoon—Mr. Gurdjieff had left Sunday evening—that the rumour that he had been in an automobile accident filtered down to the children at the school. We heard first that he had been killed, then that he had been seriously injured and was not expected to live. A formal announcement was made by someone in authority Monday evening. He was not dead, but he was seriously injured and near death in a hospital.

It is difficult to describe the impact of such an announcement. The very existence of the "Institute" depended entirely on Gurdjieff's presence. It was he who assigned work to every individual—and up to that moment he had supervised, personally, every detail of the running of the school. Now, the imminent possibility of his death brought everything to a standstill. It was only thanks to the initiative of a few of the older students, most of whom had come with him from Russia, that we continued to eat regularly.

While I did not know what was going to happen to me, personally, the one thing that was still vivid in my mind was the fact that he had told me that I was to mow the lawns "no matter what happened". It was a relief to me to have something concrete to do; a definite job that he had assigned to me. It was also the first time that I had any feeling that he was, perhaps, extraordinary. It was he who had said "no matter what happens", and his accident had happened. His injunction became that much stronger. I was convinced that he had known beforehand that "something" was going to happen, although not necessarily an automobile accident.

I was not the only one who felt that his accident was, in a sense, foreordained. The fact that he had gone to Paris alone (I was told it was the first time he had done so) was sufficient proof for most of the students. My reaction, in any event, was that it had become absolutely essential to mow the grass; I was convinced that his life, at least in part, might depend on my dedication to the task he had given me.

These feelings of mine assumed special importance when, a few days later, Mr. Gurdjieff was brought back to the Prieuré, to his room which overlooked "my" lawns, and we were told that he was in a coma and was being kept alive on oxygen. Doctors came and went at intervals; tanks of oxygen were delivered and removed; a hushed atmosphere descended over the place—it was as if we were all involved in permanent, silent prayer for him.

It was not until a day or so after his return that I was told— probably by Madame de Hartmann—that the noise of the lawn-mower would have to stop. The decision I was forced to make then was a momentous one for me. Much as I respected Madame de Hartmann, I could not forget the force with which he had made me promise to do my job. We were standing at the edge of the lawn, directly beneath the windows of his room, when I had to give her my answer. I did not reflect for very long, as I recall, and I refused, with all the force in me. I was then told that his life might actually depend on my decision, and I still refused. What surprises me now is that I was not categorically forbidden to continue, or even forcibly restrained. The only explanation that I can find for this is that his power over his pupils was such that no single individual was willing to take the responsibility of totally denying my version of what he had told me. In any case, I was not restrained; I was simply forbidden to cut the grass. I continued to cut it.

This rejection of authority, of anything less than the highest authority, was deadly serious, and I think the only thing that sustained me in it was that I was reasonably convinced that the noise of a lawn-mower would not kill anyone; also, less logically, I did feel, at the time, that his life might—inexplicably—depend on my performance of the task he had given me. These reasons, however, were no defence against the feelings of the other students (there were about one hundred and fifty people there at the time, most of them adults) who were at least equally convinced that the noise I continued to make every day could be deadly.

The conflict continued for several weeks, and each day when "no change" in his condition was reported, it became more difficult for me to begin. I can remember having to grit my teeth and overcome my own fear of what I might be doing every morning. My resolve was alternately strengthened and weakened by the attitude of the other students. I was ostracized, excluded from every other activity; no one would sit at the same table with me at meals—if I went to a table where others were sitting, they would leave the table when I sat down—and I cannot remember any one person who either spoke to me or smiled at me during those weeks, with the exception of a few of the more important adults who, from time to time, continued to exhort me to stop.

III

By MID-SUMMER, 1924, my whole life was centred on grass. By that time, I was able to mow my four lawns in a total of four days. The other things I did: taking my turn as "kitchen boy" or as "gate keeper" at the small gate house which we called the "concierge", were unimportant. I have little memory for anything other than the sound of that mowing machine.

My nightmare came to an end suddenly. Early one morning, as I was pushing the lawn mower up towards the front of the château, I looked up at Gurdjieff's windows. I always did this, as if hoping for some miraculous sign. This particular morning, I saw it at last. He was standing in the open window, looking down at me. I stopped, and stared back at him, flooded with relief. For what seemed a long time, he did not do anything. Then, with a very slow movement of his hand and arm, he brought his right hand to his lips and made a gesture which I later learned had always been characteristic of him: with his thumb and index finger, he, as it were, parted his moustache from the centre, and then his hand fell to his side and he smiled. The gesture made him real—without it, I might have thought the figure standing there simply an hallucination or a figment of my imagination.

The sensation of relief was so intense that I burst into tears, gripping the lawn mower with both of my hands. I continued to watch him through my tears until he moved slowly away from the window. And then I started to mow again. What had been the dreadful noise of that machine now became joyous to me. I pushed the lawn mower up and down, up and down, with all my strength.

I decided to wait until noon to announce my triumph, but by the time I went in to lunch I realized that I had no proof, nothing to announce, and, with what now seems surprising wisdom, I did not say anything, although I was unable to contain my happiness.

By evening, it was generally known that Mr. Gurdjieff was out of danger, and the atmosphere at dinner-time was one of gratitude and thankfulness. My part in his recovery—I had become convinced that I, alone, would be responsible in great part for whatever happened to him—was lost in the general rejoicing. All that happened was that the animosity which had been directed towards me disappeared as suddenly as it had arisen. If it had not been for the fact that I had actually, some weeks before, been forbidden to make any noise near his windows, I would have thought that the whole thing had existed only in my mind. The lack of any kind of triumph, of any recognition, was a blow.

The incident was not, however, completely closed even then. Mr. Gurdjieff appeared, warmly dressed and walking slowly, a few days later. He came to sit at the little table where he had first interviewed me. I was, as usual, trudging up and down with my lawn mower. He sat there, seemingly oblivious of everything around him, until I finished the lawn which I had been mowing that day. It was the fourth and, thanks to the impetus of his recovery, I had shortened my mowing time to three days. As I pushed the mowing machine ahead of me, taking it back to the shed where it was kept, he looked at me and motioned me to come over to him.

I dropped the lawn mower and went to stand at his side. He smiled, again I would say "benevolently", and asked me how long it took me to mow the lawns. I answered, proudly, that I could mow all of them in three days. He sighed, staring ahead of him at the expanse of grass, and stood up. "Must be able to do in one day," he said. "This important."

One day! I was appalled, and filled with mixed emotions. Not only was I given no credit for my accomplishment—at least for having, in spite of everything, kept my promise; I was practically being punished for it.

Gurdjieff paid no attention to my reactions, which must have been visible on my mobile face, but put one hand on my shoulder and leaned rather heavily on me. "This important," he repeated, "because when can cut lawns in one day, have other work for you." He then asked me to walk with him— to help him walk—to a particular field, not far away, explaining that he was unable to walk easily.

We walked together slowly, and with considerable difficulty, even with my help, we ascended a path by the field he had mentioned. It was a sloping hill, filled with rocks, near the chicken yard. He sent me into a tool shed near the chicken coops and told me to bring him the scythe, which I did. He then led me into the field, took his hand from my shoulder, took the scythe in both of his hands and made a sweeping, cutting gesture with it. As I watched him, I felt that the effort he was making was very great; I feared his pallor and his obvious weakness. He then handed the scythe back to me and told me to put it away. When I had done so, I came back to stand beside him, and once more he leaned heavily on my shoulder.

"When can cut all lawns in one day, this will be new work. Scythe this field every week."

I looked up the slope at the long grass, the rocks and trees and bushes. I was also aware of my own size—I was small for my age, and the scythe had seemed very large. All I could do was to stare at him, amazed. It was only the look in his eyes, serious and pained, that prevented me from making an immediate, angry, tearful protest. I simply bowed my head and nodded, and then walked with him, slowly, back to the main house, up the stairs and to the door of his room.

At eleven, I was no stranger to self-pity, but this development was almost too much for me. In fact, self-pity was only a small part of my feelings. I also felt anger and resentment. Not only had I had no recognition, no thanks—I was practically being punished. What kind of place was this school— and what sort of man was he, after all? Bitterly, and rather proudly, I remembered that I would be going back to America in the fall. I would show him. All that I had to do was never to manage to mow the lawns in one day!

Curiously, when my feelings subsided and I began to accept what appeared to be the inevitable, I found that my resentment and anger, although I still felt them, were not directed against Mr. Gurdjieff personally. There had been a look of sadness in his eyes as I had walked with him, and I had felt concerned about him, about his health; once again, although there had been no admonitions to the effect that I *must* do this work, I felt that I had taken on some kind of responsibility; that I would have to do it for his sake.

The following day there was another surprise in store for me. He summoned me to his room in the morning and asked me, sternly, if I was able to keep a secret—from everyone. The firmness and the fiery glance he gave me as he asked me the question were completely unlike his weakness of the day before. I assured him, valiantly, that I could. Once more I felt a great challenge—I would keep his secret no matter what!

He then told me that he did not want to worry the other students—and particularly his secretary, Madame de Hartmann—but that he was almost blind, and that I was the only one who knew this. He outlined an intriguing plot to me: He had decided to reorganize all the work then going on at the Prieuré. I was to go everywhere with him, carrying an armchair; the excuse for this being that he was still very weak, and would need to rest from time to time. The real reason, however, which was part of the secret, was that I was to follow him because he could not actually see where he was going. In short, I was to be his guide, and his caretaker; the keeper of his person.

I felt, finally, that my reward had come; that my conviction had not been a false one, and that the keeping of my promise had been as important as I had hoped. The triumph was solitary since I could not share it, but it was genuine.

IV

My new work as "chair-carrier" or, as I thought of it then, "guardian", took a great deal of my time. I was excused from all other duties with the one exception of the never-ending lawns. I was able to keep up with my mowing, but I had to do most of it before Mr. Gurdjieff appeared in the morning, or after he had retired to his room in the latter part of the afternoon.

I have never known whether or not there was any truth to his story of partial blindness. I assumed it was true because I always believed him implicitly—he seemed unable to tell anything other than the truth, although his way of telling it was not always direct. It has been suggested to me, and it also occurred to me, that this job of chair-carrier and guide was invented on my account, and that he made up the story of blindness as an excuse. I doubt this if only because it would have given me an exaggerated importance, which is a thing that I cannot imagine Gurdjieff doing. I was important enough, simply because I had been selected, without any additional reasons.

In the weeks that followed—probably a month in all— I carried that armchair for miles each day, usually following him at a respectful distance. I was sufficiently convinced of his blindness because he frequently wandered from the path, and I would have to drop the chair, run to his side, warn him of whatever danger existed—such as the possibility, often imminent, of his walking directly into the little ditch that ran through the property—and then rush back to the armchair, pick it up, and follow him again.

The work that he directed at that time involved everyone at the school. There were several projects going on at once: building a road, which meant hammering stone with iron mallets to produce the proper size rocks; clearing an area of woodland by removing entire acres of trees as well as their stumps and roots with shovels and pick-axes. In addition to such special projects, the usual duties of gardening, weeding, picking vegetables, cooking, housekeeping, etc., continued incessantly. Whenever Mr. Gurdjieff inspected a given project for any length of time, I would join in with the other workers until he was ready to proceed to another one or to return to the house.

After about a month, I was relieved of my chair-carrying assignment and went back to regular lawn-mowing, and my turn at other regular duties: working in the kitchen one day a week, standing my regular day of duty at the concierge to open the door and answer the telephone.

During my period of following him, I had had to fit my lawn-mowing in, as I have said, when I could, and it was with some consternation—since I had momentarily forgotten about the hill which I was eventually to scythe weekly—that I found that when I got back to regular work, I had, without perceptible effort, achieved the goal he had set for me. At the moment of this discovery, one evening after tea when I had finished the fourth lawn that day, Mr. Gurdjieff was seated conveniently on a bench—not at his usual table—facing the lawns. I put the lawn mower away, and came back to the terrace and walked in his direction disconsolately. While I had never loved the lawns, the prospect of my next job made me feel sentimental about them. I stopped at what I thought of as a respectful distance from him and waited. I was wavering between telling him, and putting it off until some future time.

It was some time before he turned in my direction, as if angry with my presence, and asked me sharply if I wanted something. I nodded and went up to stand beside him. I said, quickly: "I can mow all the lawns in one day, Mr. Gurdjieff."

He frowned at me, shook his head, puzzled, and then said: "Why you tell me this?" He still seemed angry with me.

I reminded him of my new "job" and then asked him, almost tearfully, if I should start on that the following day.

He stared at me for a long time then, as if unable to remember or even to understand what I was talking about. Finally, with a brusque, affectionate, gesture, he pulled me roughly towards him and forced me down on the bench next to him, keeping his hand on my shoulder. Once again he smiled at me with that distant, incredible smile—I have referred to it as "benevolent" before—and said, shaking his head, "Not necessary work in field. You have already done this work."

I looked at him, confused, and greatly relieved. But I needed to know what I was to do—continue with the lawns?

He thought about this for some time and then asked me how much longer I was going to be there. I told him that I was supposed to go back to America for the winter in about one month. He thought about this and then said, dismissing the subject as if it were unimportant now, that I would simply work in the group at the usual duties; gardening when I wasn't on kitchen or concierge duty. "Will have other work for you if you come back next year," he said.

Although I spent another month there that year, the summer seems to me to have ended at that moment. The rest of the time was like a void: uneventful and undramatic. Those of us, that is the children, who worked along with the adults in the gardens were able to make enjoyable games of picking fruit or vegetables, catching mole-crickets, slugs and snails, weeding here and there with little interest or devotion to our tasks. It was a happy place for children: we lived safely within the confines of a rigorous discipline with definite limits, and the framework—except for the long hours—was not hard on us. We managed to fit in a great deal of play and childish intrigue while the tireless adults looked at us indulgently with half-closed eyes.

V

WE LEFT THE Prieuré in October, 1924, to return to New York for the winter. I was part of a rather "unusual family group" at that time. My brother, Tom, and I lived in a strange, errant world for several years. My mother, Lois, had divorced my father when I was about eighteen months old; we had had a stepfather for several years, but in 1923, when my mother was hospitalized for about a year, Jane Heap and Margaret Anderson (Margaret is my mother's sister), co-editors of the notorious, if not famous, *Little Review*, had taken charge of us both. To this day, I am not at all sure that I understand why Margaret and Jane took on this responsibility. It was a strange form of "planned parenthood" for two women neither of whom, it seemed to me, would have wished for children of their own, and a mixed blessing from any point of view. As Margaret had not returned from France with us, the real responsibility devolved on Jane.

I can only describe our household as it seemed to me at the time: Tom and I went to a private school in New York; we also had various chores at home, helping with the cooking, dishwashing, and so on, and while we were exposed to many unusual influences and experiences, they had less effect on me, at any rate, than might have been expected. In a household, if that is the proper word, where a magazine was edited, and which was visited exclusively by artists, writers, and—for want of a better word—intellectuals, I managed to live in my own private world. The daily routine of school was considerably more important to me—involving, as it naturally did, other children and ordinary, comprehensible activities—than the temperamental and "interesting" life which, actually, formed our background. The world of the arts was no substitute for childhood; even family life with my mother and stepfather was more "normal" to me than living in New York away from my *family*, which, basically, revolved around my mother.

The most important exterior event of that winter was the sudden appearance of my father. Jane had decided, for reasons which I have never fully understood, that she (or perhaps she and Margaret) should adopt Tom and myself legally. The adoption proceedings were the reason that my father came back into the picture after a complete absence of some ten years. At first, he did not actually appear in person. We were simply told that he was going to resist the adoption and that he wanted to assume custody of both of us himself.

As I understood it at the time, Jane, aided by A. R. Orage and others who were "Gurdjieff people", and after consulting both of us, was able to talk my father out of this, and the adoption became a legal fact.

In many ways, it was a terrifying winter for me. I think it is probably impossible for any adult to understand the feelings of a child who is told, in perfectly clear language, that he may or may not be adopted by this or that person. I do not believe that children, when they are consulted about such things, have "opinions"—they naturally cling to the known, relatively safe, situation. My relationship with Jane, as I felt and experienced it, was highly volatile and explosive. There was, at times, a great deal of emotion, of love, between us, but the very emotionality of the relationship frightened me. More and more I tended to shut out everything that was outside of myself. People, for me, were something I had to exist with, had to bear. As much as possible, I lived alone, day-dreaming in my own world, longing for the time when I could escape from the complex, and often totally incomprehensible, world around me. I wanted to grow up and be alone—away from all of them. Because of this, I was almost always in trouble. I was lazy about my work at home, I resented any demands that were made on me, and any duties that I was supposed to perform, any contribution I was expected to make. Obstinate and independent because of my feeling of aloneness, I was usually in trouble, frequently punished. That winter, I began, slowly at first, but firmly, to despise my surroundings, and to hate Jane and Tom—mostly because they were there and a part of the life in which I lived. I worked well at school, but because it was easy for me, I had little real interest in what I was doing. More and more, I retreated into a dreamworld of my own making.

In this world of my own, there were two people who were not enemies, who stood out with the brilliance of lighthouses, and yet there was no way that I could communicate with them. They were my mother and, of course, Gurdjieff. Why "of course"? The simple reality of Gurdjieff as a human being—the, to me, uncomplicated relationship which I had had with him during those few months in the previous summer—became like a raft to a drowning man.

When I was consulted about the possibility of being "taken over" by my father (who was simply another hostile adult in my mind) I voiced my opposition loudly, not that I expected my voice to have any weight. My main fear was that I did not feel I could face another new, strange, unknown world. Also, and this was very important to me then, such a change in my existence would, I felt sure, preclude any possibility of my ever seeing either Gurdjieff or my mother again.

To complicate matters even further, my mother arrived in New York, with a man who was not my stepfather, and she was summarily dismissed by Jane. I remember being allowed to speak to her on the stairs of the apartment; no more than that. It is impossible for me, now, to judge Jane's motives or her purpose at that time. I am convinced that she was motivated, in her own mind, by the best of intentions. The result was that I thought of her at that moment as my mortal enemy. The link between the average child and his mother—especially when that mother has been the only parent for many years—is, I think, strong enough. In my case it was violent and obsessive.

Matters did not improve when, shortly before Christmas, my father made his actual, physical appearance. It was a difficult, uneasy meeting; there was very little communication—I speak for myself alone—with him. He did not know how to communicate without self-consciousness, being a shy and "well-brought-up" man. One thing that he did manage to communicate was that before we made any final decision about the adoption (I had been under the impression for some time that it was final and that he had been disposed of as a threat) he would like Tom and me to spend a weekend with him and his wife.

I felt that it was only fair to give him a trial. If this statement seems *cold-blooded*, I can only say that most childish decisions are, in that sense, "cold-blooded" and logical—at least mine were. It was decided, presumably by Jane and my father (and agreed to by Tom and myself), that we would go to visit him on Long Island for a week.

The visit, from my point of view, was a disaster. It might have been less calamitous had my father not announced, almost immediately upon our arrival, that in the event we should decide to come to live with him, we would not be able to live in his house, we would be sent to live in Washington, D.C., with two of his maiden aunts. I suppose that it is inevitable that adults must explain to children the actual facts or circumstances which are facing them. However, this announcement, made without any *feeling*, any emotion (there was no suggestion that he loved or wanted us, or that the aunts in question needed two young boys in their household), seemed both completely illogical and even, finally, hilarious to me. I began to feel even more alone than I had before— like a piece of unwanted luggage for which storage space was needed. Since my gentle father constantly seemed to be seeking our approval and asking us questions, I stated firmly after two days at his house that I did not want to live with him or his aunts and that I wanted to go back to New York. Tom stayed for the balance of the week; I did not. However, the condition of my leaving was that I should at least consider coming out to Long Island again, for Christmas. I agreed, coldly, to consider it. I may have—I do not remember now— agreed without any reservation. I would have done anything to get away. Even Jane, in spite of her rejection of my mother, was familiar ground; and what I feared was the unfamiliar, the unknown.

Somehow, the winter did pass. Somehow, although I frequently had nightmares about the possibility that I would never see the Prieuré again, it was decided—it was actually true—that we would return the next Spring. Gurdjieff, by this time, had become the only beacon on the horizon, the only island of safety in a fearful and unpredictable future.

During that winter, Gurdjieff's first question to me: "Why had I come to Fontainebleau" assumed tremendous importance. Retrospectively, in those few months, he assumed great stature in my heart and in my mind. Unlike any other adult I had ever known, he made absolute sense. He was completely positive—he had ordered me to do things and I had done them. He had not questioned me, forced me to make decisions which I was completely unable to make. I began to long for someone who would do something as simple as to "order" me to mow a lawn—make a demand on me that was, however incomprehensible his motives might be (after all, every adult was "incomprehensible"), a *demand*. I began to think of him as the only logical, grown-up individual I had ever known. As a child, I was not concerned with—in fact I did not want to know—*why* any adult did anything. I needed, desperately, and wanted above everything else, an authority. And an authority, at my age, was anyone who knew what he was doing. To be consulted, at eleven; to be asked to make vital decisions about my own future—and that seemed to me to have been going on all winter—was not only impossible to understand, but very frightening.

His question evolved into "Why did I want to go back to Fontainebleau" and was not difficult to answer. I wanted to go back and live near a human being who knew what he was doing—whether or not I understood what he was doing was of no importance whatsoever. I did not, however, dismiss the original wording of the question—one of the reasons it remained alive in my mind was that I had had nothing, directly, to do with going there in the first place. I could only thank whatever force (the idea of "God" was rather vague to me then) had made it possible for me to be there at all. One year earlier, the most attractive thing about going to Fontainebleau was that I would have to cross the ocean to get there, and I loved boats.

In the course of the winter, and because of the importance Gurdjieff had assumed in my mind, I was greatly tempted by the feeling that my presence there had been "inevitable"— as if there had been some inexplicable, mystical, logic that had made it necessary for me, personally, to arrive at that particular place at that particular time—that there had been some real purpose in my having gone there. The fact that Gurdjieff was primarily associated—in the conversation of most of the adults surrounding me at the time—with metaphysical activities, religion, philosophy, and mysticism, seemed to increase the possibility of some sort of foreordination in our meeting.

But in the long run, I did not succumb to the idea that my association with him was "predestined". It was my memory of Mr. Gurdjieff himself that prevented me from giving in to such daydreams. I was in no position to deny the possibility that he was clairvoyant, mystical, a hypnotist, even a "divinity". The important thing was that none of those things mattered. What did matter about him was that he was a positive, practical, sensible, logical human being. In my small mind, the Prieuré seemed the most sensible institution in the entire world. It consisted, as I saw it, of a place which housed a large number of people who were extremely busy doing the necessary physical work to keep it going. What could have been simpler and what could have made more practical sense? I was aware that, at least by repute, there were probably other benefits that could accrue from being there. But at my age, and in my terms, there was simply one aim, and a very simple one at that. To be like Gurdjieff. He was strong, honest, direct, uncomplicated—an entirely "no-nonsense" individual. I could remember, quite honestly, that I had been terrified of the work involved in mowing the lawns; it was equally apparent to me that one of the reasons for my terror was that I was lazy. Gurdjieff *made* me mow the lawns. He did not do this by threats, promises of rewards, or by asking me. He *told* me to mow the lawns. He told me it was important. I did it. One obvious result, obvious to me at eleven years of age, was that work—just plain ordinary physical work—lost a great deal of its horror for me. I also understood, although perhaps not intellectually, why I had not had to scythe the hill—why I had, as he had said, "already done it".

The total effect of the winter of 1924–25 in New York was to make me long to go back to France. The first visit there had "happened", the result of an aimless, unconnected, chain of events which had depended on my mother's divorce, her illness, the existence of Margaret and Jane and their interest in us. The return, in the spring of 1925, did seem to be foreordained. My feeling was that, if necessary, I would get there alone.

My disenchantment with, and lack of understanding of, the adult world had come to a kind of climax at Christmastime. I became (I am describing my feelings) something like a bone fought over by two dogs. The contest of wills, since my mother had been eliminated as a contender, for the custody of Tom and myself, was still waging between Jane and my father. I feel sure, now, that it was a "face-saving" operation on both sides; I cannot believe that either side wanted us for our special value—I was certainly behaving badly enough not to be particularly desirable at the time. In any case, I had agreed, or at least agreed to consider, to visit my father at Christmas. When the time for the actual decision arrived, I refused. Jane's counter-offer of an "adult" Christmas—glamorous, with parties, visits to the theatre, and so forth, was my ostensible and handy reason for refusing to visit my father. My real reason, however, remained what it had always been: Jane, however impossible our relationship might seem to me, was the passport to Gurdjieff, and I did my best to achieve some sort of harmony with her. On her side, since she was neither infallible nor inhuman, my decision—indicating an apparent preference for her—pleased her.

My father was very unhappy. I could not understand why, since I had been told that the decision was mine to make. He arrived in New York to pick up Tom—who had agreed to spend Christmas with him—and brought with him several large boxes of presents for me. I was embarrassed by the presents, but when he also asked me—and it seemed to me used the presents as bait—to reconsider, I was wounded and furious. I felt that the unfairness, the lack of "justice" in the adult world, was synthesized by this act. I told him, raging at him in tears, that I could not be bought and that I would always hate him for what he was doing to me.

For the sake of the memory of my father, I would like to digress just long enough to say that I am fully conscious of his good intentions, and that I appreciate the horrible emotional shock he received from me at the time. What was sad, perhaps even heart-breaking for him, was that he had no conception of what was really happening. In his world, children did not reject their parents.

The winter did end, finally, although I still think of it as interminable. But it did end, and with the spring my longing for the Prieuré intensified. It was not until we were actually on a ship bound for France that I believed I would really get back. And it was not until I went through the gate of the Prieuré once more that I was able to stop dreaming, believing and hoping.

When I saw him again, Gurdjieff put his hand on my head, and I looked up at his fierce moustaches, the broad, open smile underneath the shining, bald head. Like some large, warm animal, he pulled me to his side, squeezing me affectionately with his arm and hand, and said: "So . . . you come back?" It was phrased as a question, something a little more than a statement of fact. All I was able to do was to nod my head against him and contain my explosive happiness.

VI

THE SECOND SUMMER—the summer of 1925—was a home-coming. I found, as I had dreamed I would, that nothing, essentially, had changed. There were some people missing from the summer before, and some new people, but the comings and goings of individuals were of little importance. Once again, I was absorbed into the place, becoming a cog in the functioning of the school. With the exception of the mowing of the lawns, which had become some other person's task, I went back to the customary, routine chores, along with everyone else.

The great security of the Institute for a child, as opposed to the usual boarding school, for example, was the immediate feeling of belonging. It may be true that the purpose of working with other people in the maintenance of the school proper—which is what all our tasks amounted to—had a higher aim. On my level, they made me feel that I, however unimportant I might be as an individual, was one of the small, essential links that kept the school going. It gave each of us a feeling of value—of worth; I find it hard now to imagine any single thing that would be more encouraging to the ego of a child. We all felt that we had a place in the world—we were needed for the simple reason that we performed functions that had to be performed. We did not just do anything, such as study for our own benefit. We did things that had to be done for the general welfare.

In the usual sense, we had no lessons, we did not "learn" anything at all. However, we did learn to do our own washing and ironing, to cook, to milk, to chop wood, to scrape and polish floors, to paint houses, to repair roofs, to mend our clothing, to take care of animals; all these things in addition to working, in large groups, on the customary major projects: road-building, clearing wooded areas, planting and harvesting, etc.

There were two major changes at the Institute that summer, although they were not immediately apparent to me. Gurd-jieff's mother had died during the winter, which had made a subtle, emotional change in the feeling of the place—she had never taken an active part in the running of the school, but we had all been aware of her presence—and, much more important, Gurdjieff had begun to write.

I had only been there about a month, when it was announced that a complete reorganization was to be made in the way the Institute was to function and, alarming to everyone, it was also announced that for various reasons, mostly because Gurdjieff would no longer have the time or energy to supervise his students personally, not everyone would be allowed to stay on. We were also told that, in a period of the two or three days following this announcement, Gurdjieff would interview every student personally and decide whether or not they would be allowed to stay on and, if so, what they would do.

The general reaction was to drop everything and wait until each person's individual fate had been decided. After breakfast the following morning, the buildings echoed with gossip and speculation; everyone expressed his or her doubts and fears about the future. To many of the older students, the announcement seemed to mean that the school would no longer have value for them since Gurdjieff's energies would be concentrated on his writing and not on individual teaching. The speculation and the expression of fears made me nervous. Since I had no conception of what Gurdjieff might decide about my personal fate, I found it simpler to go on with my particular job of the moment—working in the clearing, removing tree stumps. Several of us had been assigned to this work, but only one or two of us went to work that morning. By the end of the day, there had been a good many interviews, and a number of students had been told to leave.

The following day, I went to my work as usual, but when I was going to return to work after lunch, my turn for an interview came.

Gurdjieff was sitting out of doors, on a bench near the main building, and I went to sit next to him. He looked at me as if surprised to find that I existed. He asked me what I had been doing, and, more particularly, what I had done since the announcements had been made. I told him, and he then asked me if I wanted to stay on at the Prieuré. I said, of course, that I did. He said, very simply, that he was glad I did because he had new work for me. Beginning the following day, I was to take care of his personal quarters—his room, dressing-room, and bathroom. He handed me a key, impressing upon me firmly that I was the only one—other than himself—who had a key, and he explained that I would have to make his bed, sweep, clean, dust, polish, wash, and generally maintain order. When the weather required, I would be responsible for making fires and keeping them going; an additional responsibility was that I would also be required to be his "server" or "waiter"—which meant that if he wanted coffee, liquor, food, or anything, brought to him at any hour of the day or night, I was to bring it. For this reason, he explained, a buzzer would be installed in my room.

He also explained that I would not participate in general projects any longer, but that my additional chores would include the usual work in the kitchen and concierge except that I would be relieved of these duties long enough to perform my housekeeping chores. One other piece of new work was that I was to take care of the chicken yard—feed the chickens, collect the eggs, slaughter the chickens and/or ducks when required, etc.

I was very proud to have been selected as his "care-taker", and he smiled at my joyful reaction. He informed me, very seriously, that my selection had been made on the spur of the moment—he had dismissed a student who had already been doing this work, and when I had appeared to be interviewed, he had realized that I was not essential in any other general function and was available for this work. I felt somewhat ashamed of my pride, but was no less happy for that, I still felt that it was an honour.

At first, I had no more contact with Gurdjieff than I had before. In the early morning, I would release the chickens from their coops, feed them and collect the eggs and bring them to the kitchen. By that time, Gurdjieff was usually ready for his morning coffee, after which he dressed and went to sit at one of the small tables near the terrace where he would spend the morning writing. During that time, I cleaned the room. This took a fairly long time. The bed was enormous and always in great disorder. As for the bathroom! What he could do to his dressing-room and bathroom is something that cannot be described without invading his privacy; I will only say that, physically, Mr. Gurdjieff, at least so I gathered, lived like an animal. The mere cleaning of these two rooms was a major project every day. The disorder was frequently so great that I had visions of great, hygienic dramas transpiring nightly in

the dressing-room and bathroom. I often felt that he had some
conscious aim to destroy these rooms. There were times when
I would have to use a ladder to clean the walls.

It was not until later that summer that my care-taking
chores began to assume really major proportions. Because of
his writing, there were many more visitors to his room—
people who were working on immediate translations of his
books—as he wrote them—into French, English, Russian, and
possibly other languages. I understood that the original was
in a combination of Armenian and Russian; as he said that
he could not find any single language which gave him sufficient freedom of expression for his complicated ideas and
theories. My additional work was mostly in the form of
"serving"—everyone who interviewed him did so in his room.
This meant the serving of coffee and Armagnac, and also
meant that the room would have to be at least straightened
up after these conferences. Gurdjieff preferred to go to bed
during such meetings. In fact, unless he was entering or
leaving the room, I hardly remember ever seeing him in his
room when he was not in the great bed, lying in state. Even
the drinking of coffee could produce a holocaust—there would
be coffee all over the room and usually in the bed, which, of
course, would have to be re-made with fresh linen each time.

There were rumours at the time, and I am in no position to
deny them, that a great deal more went on in his rooms other
than drinking coffee and Armagnac. The normal state of his
rooms after one night indicated that almost any human
activity could have taken place there the night before. There
is no doubt that his rooms were lived in, in the fullest sense
of the word.

I have never forgotten the first time that I was involved in
an incident in his room that was something more than the
usual performance of my housekeeping chores. He had a
distinguished visitor that day—A. R. Orage—a man who was
well-known to all of us, and accepted as an accredited teacher
of Gurdjieffian theory. After luncheon that day, the two of
them retired to Gurdjieff's room, and I was summoned to
deliver the usual coffee. Orage's stature was such that we all
treated him with great respect. There was no doubt of his
intelligence, his dedication, his integrity. In addition, he was
a warm, compassionate man for whom I had great personal
affection.

When I reached the doorway of Gurdjieff's room with my tray of coffee and brandy, I hesitated, appalled at the violent sounds of furious screaming—Gurdjieff's voice—from within. I knocked and, receiving no reply, entered. Gurdjieff was standing by his bed in a state of what seemed to me to be completely uncontrolled fury. He was raging at Orage, who stood impassively, and very pale, framed in one of the windows. I had to walk between them to set the tray on the table. I did so, feeling flayed by the fury of Gurdjieff's voice, and then retreated, attempting to make myself invisible. When I reached the door, I could not resist looking at both of them: Orage, a tall man, seemed withered and crumpled as he sagged in the window, and Gurdjieff, actually not very tall, looked immense —a complete embodiment of rage. Although the raging was in English I was unable to listen to the words—the flow of anger was too enormous. Suddenly, in the space of an instant, Gurdjieff's voice stopped, his whole personality changed, he gave me a broad smile—looking incredibly peaceful and inwardly quiet—motioned me to leave, and then resumed his tirade with undiminished force. This happened so quickly that I do not believe that Mr. Orage even noticed the break in the rhythm.

When I had first heard the sound of Mr. Gurdjieff's voice from outside the room I had been horrified. That this man, whom I respected above all other human beings, could lose his control so completely was a terrible blow to my feelings of respect and admiration for him. As I had walked between them to place the tray on the table, I had felt nothing but pity and compassion for Mr. Orage.

Now, leaving the room, my feelings were completely reversed. I was still appalled by the fury I had seen in Gurdjieff; terrified by it. In a sense, I was even more terrified when I left the room because I realized that it was not only *not* "uncontrollable" but actually under great control and completely conscious on his part. I still felt sorry for Mr. Orage, but I was convinced that he must have done something terrible—in Gurdjieff's eyes—to warrant the outburst. It did not cross my mind that Gurdjieff could have been, in any sense at all, wrong, There was no question but that I believed in him with my whole being, absolutely. He could do no wrong. Oddly enough, and I find this hard to explain to anyone who did not know him personally, my devotion to him was not fanatical. I did not believe in him as one believes in a god. He was right, always, to me, for simple, logical, reasons. His unusual "mode of life", even such things as the disorder of his rooms, calling for coffee at all hours of the day or night, seemed far more logical than the so-called normal way of living. He did whatever he did when he wanted or needed to. He was invariably concerned with others, and considerate of them. He never failed, for example, to thank me and to apologize to me when I had to bring him coffee, half-asleep, at three o'clock in the morning. I knew instinctively that such consideration was something far more than ordinary, acquired courtesy. And, perhaps this was the clue, he was interested. Whenever I saw him, whenever he gave me an order, he was fully aware of me, completely concentrated on whatever words he said to me; his attention never wandered when I spoke to him. He always knew exactly what I was doing, what I had done. I think we must all have felt, certainly I did, when he was with any one of us, that we received his total attention. I can think of nothing more complimentary in human relations.

VII

I$_T$ WAS IN the middle of that busy summer that Gurdjieff asked me one morning, rather brusquely, whether or not I still wanted to study. He reminded me, rather sardonically, of my desire to learn "everything", and asked me if I had changed my mind. I told him I had not.

"Why you not ask about this then, if not change mind?"

I said, embarrassed and uncomfortable, that I had not mentioned it again for several reasons. One was that I had already asked him and that I assumed that he had not forgotten it, second that he was already so busy writing and conferring with other people that I did not think he would have time.

He said that I would have to learn about the world. "If want something, must ask. You must work. You expect me to remember for you; I already work hard, much harder than you can even imagine, you wrong if also expect me always remember what you want." He then added that I made a mistake in assuming that he was too busy. "If I busy, this my business, not your affair. If I say I teach, you must remind me, help me by asking again. This show you want learn."

I agreed, sheepishly, that I had been mistaken, and asked when we would start the "lessons". This was on a Monday morning, and he told me to meet him at his room at ten o'clock the following morning, Tuesday. When I got there the next morning, I listened at the door to be sure that he was up, knocked and went in. He was standing in the middle of the room, fully dressed. He looked at me, as if astonished. "You want something?" he asked, not unkindly. I explained that I was there for my lesson. He looked at me, as he sometimes had on other occasions, as if he had never seen me before. "You supposed to come this morning?" he asked, as if he had completely forgotten. "Yes," I said, "at ten o'clock."

He looked at the clock on his bed table. It read about two minutes after ten and I had been there at least a full minute. Then he turned to me, looking at me as if my explanation had greatly relieved him: "This morning, I remember was something at ten o'clock, but forget what. Why you not here at ten o'clock?"

I looked at my own watch and said that I had been there at ten o'clock.

He shook his head. "You ten seconds late. Man can die in ten seconds. I live by my clock, not yours. If want learn from me must be here when my clock say ten o'clock. Today, no lesson."

I did not argue with him, but did gather my courage enough to ask him if that meant I would never have any "lessons" from him. He waved me away. "Certainly have lessons. Come next Tuesday ten o'clock. If necessary, can come early and wait—is way not to be late," then he added, and not without malice, "unless you too busy to wait for Master."

The following Tuesday I was there by quarter past nine. He came out of his room as I was about to knock—a few minutes before ten—smiled and told me he was glad I was on time. Then he asked me how long I had been there. I told him, and he shook his head, irritated. "I tell last week," he said, "that if not busy can come early and wait. I not tell to waste almost hour of time. Now we go." He told me to get a thermos bottle of coffee from the kitchen and to meet him at his car.

We drove a very short distance on a narrow, lightly travelled road, and Gurdjieff stopped the car. We descended and he told me to bring the coffee with me, and went to sit on a fallen tree near the edge of the road. He had stopped a hundred yards or so beyond a group of workmen who were laying a stone water-ditch at the side of the road. Their work consisted in bringing stones from either one of two large piles at the side of the road, carrying them to the unfinished section of the ditch, where other men were placing them in the dirt. We watched them silently, while Gurdjieff drank coffee and smoked, but said nothing to me. After a long time, at least half an hour, I finally asked him when the lesson would begin.

He looked at me with a tolerant smile. "Lesson begin at ten o'clock," he said. "What you see? Notice anything?"

I said that I had been watching the men, and that the only unusual thing I had noticed was that one of the men always went to the pile that was furthest from the actual work.

"Why you think he do this?"

I said I didn't know but that he seemed to be making work for himself because he had to carry the heavy stones further each time. He could just as easily have gone to the nearer pile of rock.

"Is true," Gurdjieff then said, "but must always look at all sides before make judgment. This man also have pleasant short promenade in shade along road when he return for next stone. Also, he not stupid. In one day he not carry so many stones. Always logical reason why people do thing certain way; necessary find all possible reasons before judge people."

Gurdjieff's language, although he paid very little attention to the proper tenses, was always unmistakably clear and definite. He did not say anything more, and I felt that he was, partly by his own concentration, forcing me to observe whatever was going on around me with as much concentration as I could. The rest of the hour went by rapidly, and we returned to the Prieuré; he to his writing and I to my housekeeping. I was to return the following Tuesday at the same time for the next lesson. I did not dwell on what I had—or had not—learned; I was beginning to understand that "learning" in Gurdjieff's sense did not depend on sudden or obvious results, and that one could not expect any immediate spurts of knowledge or understanding. More and more I began to have the feeling that he scattered knowledge as he lived, oblivious of whether or not it was accepted and put to any use.

The next lesson was completely unlike the first one. He told me to clean the room, everything except making the bed, while he lay in bed. He watched me all the time, making no comment until I made the fire—it was a rainy, damp summer morning and the room was cold—and when I had lighted the fire, it smoked relentlessly. I added dry wood, blew on the coals industriously, but with little success. He did not continue to watch my efforts for very long. He got out of bed suddenly, picked up a bottle of Cognac, pushed me to one side, and poured a stream of Cognac on to the small flame; the fire burst out into the room and then settled into a steady flame. Without any comment he then went into his dressing-room and dressed while I made his bed. It was not until he was ready to leave the room that he said, casually: "If want immediate, necessary result, must use any means." Then he smiled. "When I not here, you have time; not necessary use fine old Armagnac."

And that was the end of that lesson. The dressing-room, which he had demolished silently in a few minutes, took me the rest of the morning to clean.

VIII

As part of the "complete reorganization" of the school, Mr. Gurdjieff told us that he was going to appoint a "director" who would supervise the students and their activities. He made it clear that this director would report regularly to him, and that he would still be fully informed concerning everything that took place at the Prieuré. However, his personal time would be devoted almost entirely to his writing and he would spend a much larger proportion of his time in Paris.

The director turned out to be a certain Miss Madison, an English bachelor lady (as the children all called her) who had, up to that time, been mainly in charge of the flower gardens. To most of us—children, that is—she had always been a slightly comical figure. She was tall, of uncertain age, a bony, angular shape topped off by a somewhat untidy nest of fading reddish hair. She had, up to that time, stalked about the flower gardens, usually carrying a trowel and decorated with strands of raffia, knotted to her belt and flowing in streams from her waist as she walked. She took to the directorship with zeal and relish.

Although Gurdjieff had told us that we were to accord Miss Madison every respect—"as if she were myself"—I at least wondered whether she quite deserved that respect; I also suspected that he would not be as fully informed as when he had personally supervised the work. In any case, Miss Madison became a highly important figure in our lives. She began by setting up a series of rules and regulations—I have often wondered whether she had not come from an English Army family—which, ostensibly, were to simplify the work and, in general, to introduce efficiency into what she called the haphazard functioning of the school.

Since Mr. Gurdjieff was now absent at least half of each week, Miss Madison felt that I did not have enough to do simply taking care of the chickens and cleaning his room. Among other things, I was assigned to take care of our one horse and one donkey, and also to do a certain amount of work on the flower beds, under Miss Madison's immediate, personal supervision. In addition to these specific chores, I was—as was everyone else—subject to a great many general, ground-rules. No one was to leave the grounds without specific permission from Miss Madison; our rooms were to be inspected at regular intervals; in short, a general, military-style discipline was to be enforced.

A further change caused by the "reorganization" of the school was the discontinuing of the nightly demonstrations of the dances or gymnastics. There were still classes in these gymnastics, but they only lasted for an hour or so during the afternoon, and it was on rare occasions, when Gurdjieff brought weekend guests to the Prieuré, that we gave "demonstrations". Because of this, our evenings had been free all that summer, and many of us went to the town of Fontainebleau— a walk of about two miles—in the evenings. There was nothing much for children to do in town, except to go to an occasional movie or sometimes to a small country fair or carnival. This previously unsupervised—in fact, unmentioned—privilege was important to all of us. Up to that time, no one had bothered about what any of us did in our free time as long as we were present in the morning and ready to go to work. Confronted with the order that we were to have what amounted to "passes" in order to go to town—we were told that we would have to give a "good reason" for any excursion off the grounds of the school proper—we rebelled. There was no common agreement to rebel or to disregard this particular rule. As individuals, no one obeyed it; no one ever asked for a "pass".

Not only did we not ask for permission to leave the grounds, but we went to town even when we had no reason or desire to go. We did not, of course, leave by the front gate where the "passes" would have to be shown to whoever was on duty as concierge, we simply climbed the walls, going and coming. There was no immediate reaction from Miss Madison but we soon learned, although we could not imagine how it was possible, that she had an accurate record of each person's absence. We learned of the existence of this record from Mr. Gurdjieff when, on one of his returns to the Prieuré after an absence of several days, he announced to all of us that Miss Madison had "a little black book" in which she had recorded all the "misdemeanours" of the students. He also told us that he was, for the time being, reserving his own opinion about our behaviour, but reminded us that he had appointed

Miss Madison as director and that we were supposed to obey her. While it seemed to be a technical victory for Miss Madison, it was also a hollow one; he had done nothing to help her enforce her discipline.

My first difficulty with Miss Madison arose because of the chickens. One afternoon, just after Gurdjieff had left for Paris, I learned from one of the other children—I was cleaning his room at the time—that my chickens, at least several of them, had found some way out of the chicken yard and were happily tearing up Miss Madison's flower gardens. When I arrived at the scene of the destruction, Miss Madison was furiously chasing chickens all over the garden and, together, we managed to get them all back into their pen. There had not been much damage done to the flowers and I helped Miss Madison, on her orders, to repair such damage as there was. She then told me that it was my fault that the chickens had escaped because I had not kept the fences in proper order; also that I would not be allowed to leave the grounds of the Institute for a week. She added that if she found another chicken in the gardens, she would, personally, kill it.

I did repair the fences, but apparently I did not do a very good job. One or two chickens escaped the next day and went back to the flower gardens. Miss Madison kept her promise and wrung the neck of the first chicken she was able to catch. Since I had become very fond of the chickens—I had a personal relationship with each one of them and had even given them names—I took revenge on Miss Madison by destroying one of her favourite plants. In addition, for purely personal satisfaction, I also left the grounds and went to Fontainebleau that night.

Miss Madison took me seriously to task the next morning. She said that if we could not come to an understanding together, she would have to take the matter up with Mr. Gurdjieff; that she knew that he would not tolerate any flaunting of her authority. She also said that I, by this time, led the list of offenders in her little black book. My defence was to tell her that the chickens were useful and that the garden was not; that she had no right to kill my chicken. She said that I was in no position to judge what she had a right to do, and also that Mr. Gurdjieff had made it very clear that she was to be obeyed.

Since we had come to no truce or agreement, the incident was brought to Mr. Gurdjieff's attention when he returned from Paris later that week. Immediately upon his return, he was, as it were, pounced upon by Miss Madison, and closeted in his room with her for a long time. I did become anxious during that time. After all, whatever my reasons had been, I had disobeyed her, and I had no assurance that Gurdjieff was going to see things my way.

He called for coffee later that evening after supper and when I brought it to his room, he told me to sit down. Then he asked me how I was getting along and how I liked Miss Madison. Not knowing what she had told him, I replied carefully that I was getting along all right and that I supposed Miss Madison was all right, but that the Prieuré was very different when she was in charge.

He looked at me seriously: "How different?" he asked.

I replied that Miss Madison made too many rules, that there was too much discipline.

He did not say anything about this remark but then told me that Miss Madison had told him about the fracas in the flower gardens and that she had killed a chicken, and he wanted to know my version of the story. I told him how I felt about it and that I felt, particularly, that Miss Madison had no right to kill the chicken.

"What you do with dead chicken?" he asked me.

I said that I had cleaned it and taken it to the kitchen to be eaten.

He considered this, nodded, and said that I should understand, then, that the chicken after all had not been wasted; also that, while the chicken, although dead, had been useful, the dead flower that I had uprooted in anger could serve no purpose—could not, for instance, be eaten. Then he asked me if I had repaired the fences. I said that I had repaired them a second time after the chickens had escaped again and he said that was good, and sent me to get Miss Madison.

I went for her, feeling crestfallen. I could not deny the logic of what he had said to me, but I still felt, resentfully, that Miss Madison had not been entirely in the right. I found her in her room, and she gave me an all-knowing, superior look, and followed me back to Gurdjieff's room. He told us both to sit down and then told her that he had talked to me about the problem of the chickens and the garden and that he was sure—he looked at me as he said this—that there would be no more difficulty. Then he said, unexpectedly, that we had both failed him. That my failure had been in not helping him by obeying Miss Madison, since he had put her in charge, and that she had failed by killing the chicken, which was, incidentally, *his* chicken; not only was it his chicken but it was my responsibility, which he had delegated to me, and that while I should have kept it in its pen, she had no right to take its killing upon herself.

Then he told Miss Madison to leave, but added as she was leaving that he had now spent a long time, when he was already very busy, on the discussion of this matter of the chicken and the garden, and that one of the functions of a director was to relieve him of such time-consuming, unimportant problems.

Miss Madison left the room—he had indicated that I was to stay—and he asked me if I felt I was learning anything. I was surprised by the question and did not know how to answer it, except to say that I did not know. It was then, I think, that he first mentioned, directly, one of the basic purposes and aims of the Institute. He said, disregarding my unsatisfactory response to his question about learning, that, in life, the most difficult thing to achieve for the future, and perhaps the most important, was to learn to live with the "unpleasant manifestations of others". He said that the story we had both told him was, of itself, completely unimportant. The chicken and the plant did not matter. What was important was the behaviour of myself and of Miss Madison; that if either one of us had been "conscious" of our behaviour, and not simply reacting to one another, the problem would have been solved without his intervention. He said that, in a sense, nothing had happened except that Miss Madison and I had given in to our mutual hostility. He did not explain this any further, and I was confused, and told him so. He told me that I would probably understand this later in life. Then he said that I would have my lesson the following morning, although it was not a Tuesday; and apologized for the fact that he was unable to keep my lessons on a regular schedule because of his other work.

IX

WHEN I WENT for my lesson the following morning, Gurdjieff looked very tired. He said that he had been working very hard—most of the night—that writing was very hard work. He was still in bed, and he stayed there throughout the lesson.

He began by asking me about the exercise that had been given to all of us to do, and which I referred to previously as "self-observation". He said that it was a very difficult exercise to do and that he wanted me to do it, with my entire concentration, as constantly as possible. He also said that the main difficulty with this exercise, as with most exercises that he did—or would in the future—give to me or to any of his students, was that to do them properly it was necessary not to expect results. In this specific exercise, what was important was to see oneself, to observe one's mechanical, automatic, reactionary behaviour without comment, and without making any attempt to change that behaviour. "If change," he said, "then will never see reality. Will only see change. When begin to know self, then change will come, or can make change if wish—if such change desirable."

He went on to say that his work was not only very difficult, but could also be very dangerous for some people. "This work not for everyone," he said. "For example, if wish to learn to become millionaire, necessary to devote all early life to this aim and no other. If wish to become priest, philosopher, teacher, or businessman, should not come here. Here only teach *possibility* how become man such as not known in modern times, particularly in western world."

He then asked me to look out of the window and to tell him what I saw. I said that, from that window, all I could see was an oak tree. And what, he asked, was on the oak tree? I told him: acorns.

"How many acorns?"

When I replied, rather uncertainly, that I did not know, he said impatiently: "Not exactly, not ask that. *Guess* how many!"

I said that I supposed there were several thousand of them.

He agreed and then asked me how many of the acorns would become oak trees. I answered that I supposed only five or six of them would actually develop into trees, if that many.

He nodded. "Perhaps only one, perhaps not even one. Must learn from Nature. Man is also organism. Nature make many acorns, but possibility to become tree exist for only few acorns. Same with man—many men born, but only few grow. People think this waste, think Nature waste. Not so. Rest become fertilizer, go back into earth and create possibility for more acorns, more men, once in while more tree—more real man. Nature always give—but only give possibility. To become real oak, or real man, must make effort. You understand this, my work, this Institute, not for fertilizer. For real man, only. But must also understand fertilizer necessary to Nature. Possibility for real tree, real man also depend just this fertilizer."

After a rather long silence, he continued: "In west—your world—is belief that man have soul, given by God. Not so. Nothing given by God, only Nature give. And Nature only give possibility for soul, not give soul. Must acquire soul through work. But, unlike tree, man have many possibilities. As man now exist he have also possibility grow by accident—grow wrong way. Man can become many things, not just fertilizer, not just real man: can become what you call 'good' or 'evil', not proper things for man. Real man not good or evil—real man only conscious, only wish acquire soul for proper development."

I had listened to him, concentrated and straining, and my only feeling—I was twelve then—was one of confusion, incomprehension. I sensed and felt the importance of what he was saying, but I did not understand it. As if aware of this (as he surely was), he said: "Think of good and evil like right hand and left hand. Man always have two hands—two sides of self— good and evil. One can destroy other. Must have aim to make both hands work together, must acquire third thing: thing that make peace between two hands, between impulse for good and impulse for evil. Man who all 'good' or man who all 'bad' is not whole man, is one-sided. Third thing is conscience; possibility to acquire conscience is already in man when born; this possibility given—free—by Nature. But is only possibility. Real conscience can only be acquired by work, by learning to understand self first. Even your religion—western religion—

have this phrase 'Know thyself'. This phrase most important in all religions. When begin know self already begin have possibility become genuine man. So first thing must learn is know self by this exercise, self-observation. If not do this, then will be like acorn that not become tree—fertilizer. Fertilizer which go back in ground and become possibility for future man."

X

As if by some settling process, Miss Madison's directorship became, automatically, something that we managed to live with without further difficulty. There was too much work to be done, ordinary labour to keep the school functioning, for anyone to care very much about rules and regulations, or about how the work was accomplished. Also, there were too many people there, and the physical set-up was too big, for Miss Madison (who had not given up her never-ending gardening) to be able to observe each of us constantly and individually. The only other incident in which Miss Madison and I found ourselves in conflict that summer—sufficient conflict to come to Mr. Gurdjieff's attention—was the incident of the Japanese garden.

At some time in the past, long before I had been at the Prieuré, one of Mr. Gurdjieff's projects had been to build what he had called a "Japanese Garden". An island had been created in the woods, using water from the ditch that ran through the property. A small, six- or eight-sided oriental-looking pavilion had been built on the island, and a typical Japanese, arched bridge led to the island proper. It looked rather typically oriental, and was a pleasant place to retire to on Sundays when we were not on duty at one of our usual tasks. One of the students—an adult American man—went there with me one Sunday afternoon; he was a recent arrival at the Prieuré and, if I remember correctly, our reason for being there was that I was serving as his guide to the physical layout of the school. It was the usual practice at that time for one of the children to walk all over the seventy-five acres of the grounds with new arrivals, showing them the various vegetable gardens, the Turkish bath, the location of current projects, and so on.

My companion and I stopped to rest at the Japanese garden and he, as if sneering at the garden, told me that while it might be "Japanese" in intention, it was completely ruined by the presence, just in front of the door to the little pavilion, of two plaster busts, one on either side of the door, of Venus and

Apollo. My reaction was immediate and angry. Also, in some curious way, I felt that the criticism of the busts was a personal criticism of Gurdjieff's taste. With mixed motives and considerable daring, I told him that I would remedy the situation and promptly threw the two busts into the water. I remember feeling that, in some obscure way, I was defending Gurdjieff's honour and his taste by doing so.

Miss Madison, whose sources of information had always been a puzzle to me, learned of this. She told me, horrified, that this wilful destruction of the busts could not pass unnoticed and that Mr. Gurdjieff would be informed of what I had done immediately upon his return from Paris.

As his next return from Paris was on a weekend, he was accompanied by several guests who came with him in his car, plus a good many additional guests who had come in their own cars or by train. As was customary on the days that he returned from his trips, the entire student-body assembled after dinner in the main salon of the Château. In the presence of everyone (it was rather like a stockholders' meeting) he received a formal report from Miss Madison covering the general events that had transpired during his absence. This report was then followed by a summary, from Miss Madison, of whatever problems had arisen that she felt needed his attention. She sat beside him, on this occasion, little black book firmly open on her lap, and talked to him earnestly, but not loudly enough for us to hear, for a short time. When she had finished, he waved her to a chair and asked whoever had destroyed the statues in the Japanese garden to step forward.

Embarrassed by the presence of all of the students as well as a number of distinguished guests, I stepped forward with a sinking heart, furious with myself for my abandoned gesture. At that moment, I could think of no justification for what I had done.

Gurdjieff, of course, asked me why I had committed this crime, and also whether I realized that the destruction of property was, in fact, criminal? I said that I realized that I should not have done it but that I had done it because the statues were of the wrong period and civilization, historically, and that they should not have been there in the first place. I did not involve the American in my explanation.

With considerable sarcasm, Gurdjieff informed me that

while my knowledge of history might be impressive, I had, nonetheless, destroyed "statues" that had belonged to him; that he, personally, had been responsible for placing them there; that, in fact, he liked Greek statues in Japanese gardens— at any rate in that particular Japanese garden. In view of what I had done, he said that I would have to be punished, and that my punishment would consist of giving up my "chocolate money" (his term for any child's "spending money" or "allowance") until the statues were replaced. He instructed Miss Madison to find out the cost of equivalent replacements and to collect that amount from me, however long it might take.

Mostly because of my family situation—Jane and Margaret had almost no money at the time, and certainly none to give to us—I had no so-called "chocolate money"; at least, I had none on what could be called a regular basis. The only spending money I ever had at that time was occasional money that my mother would send to me from America—for my birthday or for Christmas, or sometimes for no obvious reason. At that particular moment, I had no money at all, and I was also sure that the statues would be hideously expensive. I foresaw an eternity of handing over whatever money might come my way in order to pay for my rash act. It was a horrible prospect, particularly as I had had a birthday only a few months earlier and Christmas was several months in the future.

My dismal, moneyless future came to an abrupt end when I received a completely unexpected cheque for twenty-five dollars from my mother. Before turning the cheque over to Miss Madison, I learned from her that the "statues" were common, plaster casts, and would only amount to about ten dollars. Even that amount was not easy for me to part with. The twenty-five dollars might have to last me at least until Christmas.

At the next assembly, Miss Madison informed Mr. Gurdjieff that I had given her the money for the new "statues"—he refused even to understand the word "bust"—and asked whether she should replace them.

Gurdjieff thought this question over for some time and then, finally, said "No". He called me over to him, handed me the money which she had given to him, and said that I could keep it, on the condition that I would share it with all the other children. He also said that while I had been wrong in destroying his property, he wanted me to know that he had thought about the whole question and that I had been right about the impropriety of those particular "statues" in that place. He suggested that I could have—although I was not to do so now—replaced them with the proper type of statue. The incident was never mentioned again.

XI

TOWARDS THE END of the summer, I learned that Mr. Gurdjieff was making plans to go to America for an extended visit—probably the entire winter of 1925-26. The question of what was going to happen to Tom and myself automatically came to my mind, but this was quickly solved: to my great relief, Jane told us that she had decided that she would have to go back to New York but that Tom and I would stay on at the Prieuré that winter. She took us to Paris with her one weekend and introduced us to Gertrude Stein and Alice B. Toklas; Jane had somehow persuaded Gertrude and Alice to, as it were, watch over us during her absence.

On our occasional visits to Paris, we had met many controversial and distinguished people: James Joyce, Ernest Hemingway, Constantin Brancusi, Jacques Lipschitz, Tristan Tzara, and others—most of whom had been contributors at one time or another to *The Little Review*. Man Ray had photographed both of us; Paul Tchelitchev had attempted portraits of us both. I remember when Tchelitchev, after two or three consecutive days of work on a pastel portrait of me, threw me out of his studio, telling me that I was unpaintable. "You look like everyone," he had said, "and your face is never quiet."

I was either too young or too self-involved at that time to be fully conscious of the privilege, if that is the word, of knowing or meeting such people. In general, they did not make a very strong impression on me; I did not understand their conversation, and was aware of their importance only because I had been told they were important.

Of all such people, Hemingway and Gertrude Stein did stand out as genuinely impressive to me. At our first meeting with Hemingway, whose *A Farewell to Arms* had not yet been published, he impressed us with his stories of bull-fighting in Spain; with great exuberance he ripped off his shirt to show us his "battle-scars" and then fell to his hands and knees, still stripped to the waist, to play at being a bull with his first child, still only a baby at that time.

But it was Gertrude Stein who made the greatest impact on

me. Jane had given me something of hers to read—I do not know what it was—and I had found it totally meaningless; for that reason I was vaguely alarmed at the prospect of meeting her. I liked her immediately. She seemed uncomplicated, direct, and enormously friendly. She told us—she, too, had a "no-nonsense" quality about her that appealed to me as a child—that we were to visit her every other Thursday during the coming winter, and that our first visit would be on Thanksgiving Day. Although I was worried about Gurdjieff's absence—I felt that the Prieuré could not possibly be the same without him—my immediate liking of Gertrude and the knowledge that we would be seeing her regularly was considerable consolation.

Gurdjieff only spoke to me directly about his forthcoming trip on one occasion. He said that he was going to leave Miss Madison in full charge and that it would be necessary for me—as well as for everyone else—to work with her. Miss Madison no longer troubled or frightened me, I was getting used to her, and I assured him that I would do my best. He then said that it was important to learn to get along with people. Important in one way only—to learn to live with all kinds of people and in all kinds of situations; to live with them in the sense of not reacting to them constantly.

Before his departure, he called a meeting of certain of the students and Miss Madison; only those students, mostly Americans, who were going to stay at the Prieuré during his absence—excluding his own family and a few of the older students, or followers, who had been with him for many years and who, apparently, were not subject to Miss Madison's discipline. I had the feeling that Gurdjieff's immediate family, his brother, sister-in-law and their children, were not so much "followers" or "students" as simply "family" that he supported.

At this gathering, or meeting, Miss Madison served tea to all of us. It seems to me now that this was her idea, also that she was making an attempt to "put her best foot forward" with those students who would be in her charge during the winter to come. We all listened as she and Mr. Gurdjieff discussed various aspects of the functioning of the Institute—mostly practical problems, work assignments, and so forth, but the one outstanding memory of that meeting was the serving of the tea by Miss Madison. Instead of sitting in one place, pouring the tea, and handing it to us, she poured each cup, standing, and then brought it to each person. She had, unfortunately for her, a physical habit—it was sufficiently delicate, actually, to seem to be a kind of refinement—of faintly passing wind each time that she stooped over, which she had to do as she handed each person his or her cup of tea. Inevitably, there would be a rather faint, single, report at which she would immediately say "Pardon me" and stand up.

We were all amused and embarrassed by this, but no one was more amused than Gurdjieff. He watched her attentively, the faint beginning of a smile on his face, and it was impossible not to watch him as we all "listened" to Miss Madison. As if unable to control himself any longer, he began to talk. He said that Miss Madison was a very special person, with many qualities that might not be immediately apparent to the casual onlooker (he could be very verbose and flowery in the English language when he chose). As an example of one of her qualities, he cited the fact that she had a particularly exceptional manner of serving tea. That only Miss Madison served tea with the accompaniment of a small, sharp report, like that of a toy gun. "But so delicate, so refined," he said, "that it is necessary to be alert, and highly perceptive, even to be aware of this." He went on to remark that we should notice her extreme politeness: that she unfailingly excused herself after each report. He then compared this "grace" of hers with other social graces, stating that it was not only unusual but, to him, even with his wide experience, completely novel.

It was impossible not to admire Miss Madison's composure during this merciless, lengthy comment on her unfortunate habit. While it was obviously "farting", none of us could bring ourselves, even in our own minds, to the use of that gross word. As Gurdjieff talked about it, the habit became practically "endearing" to us, making us feel sympathetic and tender towards Miss Madison. The "end result" as someone punned mercilessly, was that we all felt a spontaneous, genuine liking for Miss Madison that none of us had felt before. I have often wondered since then whether or not Gurdjieff was not making use of a minor weakness in Miss Madison's seemingly impervious "armour" for the very purpose of bringing her down from the level of strict "director" to a more human conception in the minds of those of us who were present. It was certainly impossible for us to take Miss Madison too seriously from that time on; it was also equally impossible to dislike her with any great intensity—she seemed, from then on, far too human, and too fallible. For my own part, I have never heard a delicate "fart" in my life since then, without it being accompanied, in my mind, by a rather tender memory of Miss Madison.

I will not now state that Miss Madison's wind-passing made me learn to actually love her, but it certainly came close to achieving that goal. There were times when we were able to work together without difficulty or animosity, and I attribute all of those periods to her habit, or at least to my memory of it. It was and is impossible for me to whole-heartedly despise anyone who is, for any reason, a comic figure. There was a pathetic aspect to this "farting", and since the habit is relatively universal, we were inevitably laughing at ourselves, as well, when we poked fun at her behind her back. Even the phrase, as we were always doing things "behind her back", had immediate, hilarious connotations. In fact nothing could have been more appropriate for her. Even her "reports", or the mention of them, was enough to send us off into gales of laughter. And as children, we, of course, made up elaborate, merciless jokes about the possibility of the walls of her room collapsing from a constant barrage.

For her own part, Miss Madison continued to direct the activities of the school, busy, stern, and dedicated; and with occasional sharp reports, like punctuation, always accompanied by a bland apology.

XII

WITHOUT GURDJIEFF, THE Prieuré was a different place; but it was not only his absence that made it so. The very winter changed the tempo and the routine. We all settled into what seemed, in comparison with the busy active summer, a kind of hibernation. There was little or no work at all on outside "projects" and most of our duties were confined to such things as working our turns in the kitchen—much more frequent because there were so many fewer people there—in the concierge, chopping wood and transporting it to our rooms, keeping the house clean, and, in my case, finally some studies in the usual sense of the word. One of the students who had remained for the winter was an American recently graduated from college. Almost every evening, sometimes for several hours at a time, I studied the English language with him and also mathematics. I read voraciously, as if I had been starving for that kind of learning, and we went through all of Shakespeare as well as such books as the Oxford books of English Verse and English Ballads. On my own, I read Dumas, Balzac, and great many of the other French writers.

The outstanding experiences of the winter, however, were all due to Gertrude Stein and, in a lesser way, to Alice Toklas.

Our first visit to Paris to see Gertrude was a memorable one. While we were happy enough to be at the Prieuré, there was still no question but that Tom and I both missed many things that were essentially American. That first visit was on Thanksgiving Day, a holiday that, of course, meant nothing to the French or to the students at the Prieuré. We arrived at Gertrude's apartment on the rue de Fleurus at about ten o'clock in the morning. We rang the bell, but there was no answer. Alice, apparently, had gone somewhere, and Gertrude, we learned shortly, was in the bath on the second floor. When I rang the second time, Gertrude's head appeared above me, and she tossed a bunch of keys out of the window. We were to make ourselves at home in the salon until she had had her bath. As this occurred every time we went to Paris, it was obvious that Gertrude took a bath every day at just that hour, or at least every other Thursday.

A large part of the day was spent in a thoroughly enjoyable, long talk with Gertrude. I realized, later, that it was really a cross-examination. She asked us about our entire lives, our family history, our relationship with Jane and with Gurdjieff. We answered in full detail and Gertrude, patiently and without comment, never interrupted except to ask another question. We talked until late in the afternoon when Alice suddenly appeared to announce dinner—I had by that time forgotten that it was Thanksgiving—and Gertrude put us to work setting the table.

I have never known such a Thanksgiving feast in my life. It must, I suppose, have been enhanced by the fact that it was completely unexpected, but the amount and quality of the food amounted to a spectacle. I was very moved when I learned that most of the traditional, American foods—including sweet potatoes, pumpkin pie, marshmallows, cranberries, all unheard of in Paris—had been specially ordered from America for this dinner and for us.

In her usual direct, positive way, Gertrude said that she felt that American children needed to have an American Thanksgiving. She also voiced some rather positive doubts about the way we were living. She was suspicious of both Jane and Gurdjieff as "foster parents" or "guardians" of any children, and told us forcefully that she was going to take a hand in our upbringing and education, beginning with our next visit. She added that life with "mystics" and "artists" might be all very well, but that it amounted to nonsense as a steady diet for two young American boys. She said that she would work out a plan for our future visits with her that would, at least in her mind, make more sense. We left Paris that evening, late, to return to Fontainebleau and I can still recall the warmth and happiness I felt in the experience of the day, and particularly my strong feelings of affection for both Gertrude and Alice.

Gertrude's plan, as she outlined it to us on our next visit, was an exciting one. She said that I was doing enough studying and reading and that while there might be some vague rewards for us in meeting intellectuals and artists, she felt very strongly that we had one opportunity that we must not neglect: the chance to get to know, intimately, the City of Paris. She made it clear that she thought this was important for many reasons, among them that exploring and getting to know a city was a comprehensible activity for children of our age, and something that would leave its mark on us forever, also that it had been neglected shamefully. She felt that there would be time enough for us in the future, when we were at least more grown up, to delve into more nebulous pursuits, such as the arts.

We began on a series of expeditions which continued throughout the whole winter—barring days when weather prevented, which were few. We piled into Gertrude's Model-T Ford—Gertrude at the wheel and Alice and Tom squeezed into the front seat with her, while I sat next to Gertrude on the tool box on the left running board of the car. My job on these expeditions was to blow the horn at Gertrude's command. This required my full attention because Gertrude drove her little, old car majestically, approaching intersections and corners unhesitatingly and with repeated announcements (by me) on the horn.

Little by little, we did Paris. The monuments came first: Nôtre-Dame, Sacré-Coeur, the Invalides, the Tour Eiffel, the Arc de Triomphe, the Louvre (from the outside at first— we had seen enough paintings for a while in Gertrude's opinion), the Conciergerie, the Sainte Chapelle.

When we visited any monument or building that did, or could, involve climbing, Gertrude invariably handed me a red silk scarf. I was instructed to climb (in the case of the Eiffel Tower I was allowed to take the elevator) to the top of the given monument of the day and then wave to Gertrude from its summit with the red scarf. There was no question of lack of trust. She said, unequivocally, that children were all lazy. She would be able to prove to her own conscience that I had actually made the climb when she saw the red scarf fluttering from some tower or other. During these climbs, she and Alice remained seated in the Ford in some conspicuous place below us.

From buildings, we graduated to parks, squares, boulevards, important streets and on special occasions longer excursions to Versailles and Chantilly—any place that could be fitted into a comfortable one-day journey. Our days were always climaxed by a fabulous meal which had always been prepared by Alice. Generally, she managed to prepare something for us in advance, but there were times when her dedication to culinary art was such that she felt that she was unable to accompany us. In her way, Alice was giving us a gastronomic education.

From these excursions I have retained a feeling about, and a flavour of, Paris that I would never have experienced otherwise. Gertrude would lecture us about each place we visited, giving us the highlights of its history, bringing to life the famous people of the past who had created, or lived in, the places we visited. Her lectures were never over-long, never boring; she had a particular talent for re-creating the feeling of a place as she talked—she could bring buildings to life. She taught me to look for history as I lived, and urged me to explore Fontainebleau on my free days from the Prieuré. She told me much of its history before I went there, and, sensibly, said that there was no reason for her to accompany me there since it was in our backyard.

I have never forgotten that winter. The long evenings of reading and study in our warm rooms, the more or less casual day-to-day living at the Prieuré, the continual looking forward to my visits to Paris with Gertrude and Alice. The one sombre, harsh note during the winter was the occasional reminder, by Miss Madison, of the fact that I was, somehow, shirking at least some of my duties. She warned me that I was again heading the list in the black book she still kept relentlessly, but I was heedless of her warnings. Thanks primarily to Gertrude, and secondarily to my reading, I was living in the past—walking with history and Kings and Queens.

XIII

In addition to the group of children, Mr. Gurdjieff's relatives, and a few adult Americans, the only people who had not gone to America with Mr. Gurdjieff were older people—mostly Russians—who did not seem to fit into the category of students. I did not know why they were there except that they appeared to be what might be called "hangers-on", practically camp-followers. It was difficult, if not impossible, to imagine that they were in any sense interested in Gurdjieff's philosophy; and they constituted, along with Gurdjieff's family, what we called simply "The Russians". They seemed to represent the Russia that no longer existed. Most of them, I gathered, had escaped from Russia (they were all "White" Russians) with Gurdjieff, and they were like an isolated remnant of a prior civilization, justifying their existence by working, without any apparent purpose, at whatever chores were given them, in return for which they received food and shelter.

Even during the active summers, they led their own, private existence: reading the Russian newspapers, discussing Russian politics, gathering together to drink tea in the afternoons and evenings, living like displaced persons in the past, as if unaware of the present or the future. Our only contact with them was at meals and at the Turkish baths, and very occasionally they did participate in some of the group work projects.

Notable among these "refugees" was one man, about sixty years of age, by the name of Rachmilevitch. He was distinguished from "The Russians" because he was inexhaustibly curious about everything that took place. He was a mournful, dour type, full of prophecies of disaster, dissatisfied with everything. He complained, continually, about the food, the conditions in which we lived—the water was never hot enough, there was not enough fuel, the weather too cold or too hot, people were unfriendly, the world was coming to an end; in fact anything at all—any event, or any condition—was something that he seemed to be able to turn into a calamity or, at least, an impending disaster.

The children, filled with energy, and without enough to

occupy them during the long winter days and evenings, seized on Rachmilevitch as a target for their unused vitality. We all mocked him, aped his mannerisms, and did our best to make his life one long, continuous, living hell. When he would enter the dining-room for a meal, we would begin on a series of complaints about the food; when he attempted to read his Russian newspaper, we would invent imaginary political crises. We withheld his mail when we were on concierge duty, hid his newspapers, stole his cigarettes. His unending complaints had also irritated the other "Russians" and, subversively, they not only did nothing to restrain us, but, subtly and without ever mentioning his name directly, approved, and urged us on.

Not content with badgering him during the day, we took to staying up at night at least until he had turned off the light in his room; then we would gather in the corridor outside his bedroom door and have loud conversations with each other about him, disguising our voices in the hope that he would not be able to pick out any individuals among our group.

Unfortunately, and understandably, he was not able to disregard our activities—we never gave him a moment's peace. He would appear at meals, enraged by our night-time excursions in the halls, and complain in a loud voice about all of us, calling us devils, threatening to punish us, vowing to get even with us.

Seeing that no other adults—not even Miss Madison—sympathized with him, we felt emboldened, and were delighted with his reactions to us. We "borrowed" his glasses, without which he was unable to read—when he hung out his clothes to dry, we hid them, and we waited for his next appearance and his violent, raging, frustrated reactions with great anticipation and delight, moaning in a body with him as he complained about and raged at us.

The torture of Rachmilevitch came to a climax, and an end, when we decided to steal his false teeth. We had often mimicked him when he was eating—he had a way of sucking on these teeth, which made them click in his mouth—and we would imitate this habit to the great amusement of most of the other people present. There was something so whole-heartedly mischievous about our behaviour that it was difficult for anyone not to participate in our continually high, merry, malicious spirits. Whenever poor Rachmilevitch was present in any group, invariably his very presence would make all the children begin to giggle, irresistibly and infectiously. His very appearance was enough to start us laughing uncontrollably.

Whether I volunteered for the teeth-stealing mission or whether I was chosen, I no longer remember. I do remember that it was a well-planned group project, but that I was the one who was to do the actual stealing. To accomplish this, I was secreted in the corridor outside his room one night. A group of five or six of the other children proceeded to make various noises outside his room: wailing, blowing through combs which had been wrapped in toilet paper, pretending we were ghosts and calling out his name mournfully, predicting his immediate death, and so on. We kept this up interminably and as we had foreseen, he was unable to contain himself. He came tearing out of the room, in the dark, in his nightshirt, screaming in helpless rage, chasing the group down the corridor. This was my moment: I rushed into his room, seized the teeth from the glass in which he kept them on the table by his bed, and rushed out with them.

We had had no plan as to what to do with them—we had not gone so far as to think that we might keep them forever—and after a long consultation, we decided to hang them on the gas fixture above the dining-room table.

We were, of course, all present the following morning, eagerly awaiting his appearance and squirming in anticipation. No one could have been a more satisfactory target for our machinations: as expected, he came into the dining-room, his face shrunken around the mouth by his lack of teeth, the very living embodiment of frustrated rage. He lashed out at us verbally and physically, until the dining-room was in an uproar as he chased us around the table, demanding in high-pitched screams the return of his teeth. All of us, as if unable to stand the combination of suspense and delight, began casting glances upward, above the table, and Rachmilevitch finally calmed down for long enough to look up and see his teeth, hanging from the gas fixture. Accompanied by our triumphant shouts of laughter, he got up on the table and removed them and replaced them in his mouth. When he sat down again, we realized that we had—for once—gone too far.

He managed to eat his breakfast with a certain cold, silent, dignity, but although we continued, as if our motors were running down, to poke fun at him rather listlessly, our hearts were not in it any longer. He looked at us coldly, with a feeling that was even beyond hatred—the look in his eyes was like that of a wounded animal. He did not, however, let it go at that. He took the matter up with Miss Madison, who then cross-questioned us unendingly. I finally admitted to the actual theft, and although we all received black marks in her little black book, she informed me that I now led the list by an enormous margin. She kept me on in her room when she had dismissed the other children, to enumerate the list of things which she had marked up against me. I did not keep the stables sufficiently clean; I did not sweep the courtyard regularly; I did not keep Gurdjieff's room properly dusted; the chicken yard was a general mess; I was careless about my own room, my clothes and my appearance. In addition, she felt sure that I was the ring-leader in all the offences that had been committed against poor old Mr. Rachmilevitch.

As it was already early in the spring and Gurdjieff's arrival from America was imminent, I did pay some attention to her words. I cleaned up the chicken-yard, and made at least a small improvement in most of my jobs generally, but I was still living in some sort of dreamworld and I put off as many things as I could. When we learned that Gurdjieff was going to arrive on a particular day—it was told to us the morning of the very day that he was to reach the Prieuré—I surveyed the condition of my various chores and I was horrified. I realized that it would be impossible for me to get everything in order before he arrived. I concentrated on cleaning his rooms thoroughly, and sweeping the courtyard; my most "visible" projects. And, filled with guilt, instead of dropping my work when I knew he was arriving, I continued sweeping the court-yard, and did not go to greet him as everyone else had done. To my horror, he sent for me. I went to join the group, shame-facedly, expecting some immediate retribution for my sins, but he only embraced me warmly and said that he had missed me and that I was to help take his baggage up to his room and bring him coffee. It was a temporary reprieve, but I dreaded what was to come.

XIV

THE SATURDAY EVENING after Gurdjieff's return from America, which had been in the middle of the week, was the first general "assembly" of everyone at the Prieuré, in the study-house. The study-house was a separate building, originally an airplane hangar. There was a linoleum-covered raised stage at one end. Directly in front of the stage there was a small, hexagonal fountain, equipped electrically so that various coloured lights played on the water. The fountain was generally used only during the playing of music on the piano which was to the left of the stage as one faced it.

The main part of the building, from the stage to the entrance at the opposite end, was carpeted with oriental rugs of various sizes, surrounded by a small fence which made a large, rectangular open space. Cushions, covered by fur rugs, surrounded the sides of this rectangle in front of the fence, and it was here that most of the students would normally sit. Behind the fence, at a higher level, were built-up benches, also covered with Oriental rugs, for spectators. Near the entrance of the building there was a small cubicle, raised a few feet from the floor, in which Gurdjieff habitually sat, and above this there was a balcony which was rarely used and then only for "important" guests. The cross-wise beams of the ceiling had painted material nailed to them, and the material hung down in billows, creating a cloud-like effect. It was an impressive interior— with a church-like feeling about it. One had the impression that it would be improper, even when it was empty, to speak above a whisper inside the building.

On that particular Saturday evening, Gurdjieff sat in his accustomed cubicle, Miss Madison sat near him on the floor with her little black book on her lap, and most of the students sat around, inside the fence, on the fur rugs. New arrivals and "spectators" or guests were on the higher benches behind the fence. Mr. Gurdjieff announced that Miss Madison would go over all the "offences" of all the students and that proper "punishments" would be meted out to the offenders. All of the children, and perhaps I, especially, waited with bated breath as Miss Madison read from her book, which seemed to have been arranged, not alphabetically, but according to the number of offences committed. As Miss Madison had warned me, I led the list, and the recitation of my crimes and offences was a lengthy one.

Gurdjieff listened impassively, occasionally glancing at one or another of the offenders, sometimes smiling at the recital of a particular misdemeanour, and interrupting Miss Madison only to take down, personally, the actual number of individual black marks. When she had completed her reading, there was a solemn, breathless silence in the room and Gurdjieff said, with a heavy sigh, that we had all created a great burden for him. He said then that he would give out punishments according to the number of offences committed. Naturally, I was the first one to be called. He motioned to me to sit on the floor before him and then had Miss Madison re-read my offences in detail. When she had finished, he asked me if I admitted all of them. I was tempted to refute some of them, at least in part, and to argue extenuating circumstances, but the solemnity of the proceedings and the silence in the room prevented me from doing so. Every word that had been uttered had dropped on the assemblage with the clarity of a bell. I did not have the courage to voice any weak defence that might have come to my mind, and I admitted that the list was accurate.

With another sigh, and shaking his head at me as if he was very much put upon, he reached into his pocket and pulled out an enormous roll of bills. Once again, he enumerated the number of my crimes, and then laboriously peeled off an equal number of notes. I do not remember exactly how much he gave me—I think it was ten francs for each offence—but when he had finished counting, he handed me a sizeable roll of francs. During this process, the entire room practically screamed with silence. There was not a murmur from anyone in the entire group, and I did not even dare to glance in Miss Madison's direction.

When my money had been handed to me, he dismissed me and called up the next offender and went through the same process. As there were a great many of us, and there was not one individual who had not done something, violated some rule during his absence, the process took a long time. When he had gone through the list, he turned to Miss Madison and handed her some small sum—perhaps ten francs, or the equivalent of one "crime" payment—for her, as he put it, "conscientious fulfilment of her obligations as director of the Prieuré."

We were all aghast; we had been taken completely by surprise, of course. But the main thing we all felt was a tremendous compassion for Miss Madison. It seemed to me a senselessly cruel, heartless act against her. I have never known Miss Madison's feelings about this performance; except for blushing furiously when I was paid, she showed no obvious reaction to anything at all, and even thanked him for the pittance he had given her.

The money that I had received amazed me. It was, literally, more money than I had ever had at one time in my life. But it also repelled me. I could not bring myself to do anything with it. It was not until a few days later, one evening when I had been summoned to bring coffee to Gurdjieff's room, that the subject came up again. I had had no private, personal contact with him—in the sense of actually talking to him, for instance— since his return. That evening—he was alone—when I had served him his coffee, he asked me how I was getting along; how I felt. I blurted out my feelings about Miss Madison and about the money that I felt unable to spend.

He laughed at me and said cheerfully that there was no reason why I should not spend the money any way I chose. It was my money, and it was a reward for my activity of the past winter. I said I could not understand why I should have been rewarded for having been dilatory about my jobs and having created only trouble.

Gurdjieff laughed again and told me that I had much to learn.

"What you not understand," he said, "is that not everyone can be troublemaker, like you. This important in life—is ingredient, like yeast for making bread. Without trouble, conflict, life become dead. People live in status-quo, live only by habit, automatically, and without conscience. You good for Miss Madison. You irritate Miss Madison all time—more than anyone else, which is why you get most reward. Without you, possibility for Miss Madison's conscience fall asleep. This money should really be reward from Miss Madison, not from me. You help keep Miss Madison alive."

I understood the actual, serious sense in which he meant what he was saying, but I said that I felt sorry for Miss Madison, that it must have been a terrible experience for her when she saw us all receiving those rewards.

He shook his head at me, still laughing. "You not see or understand important thing that happen to Miss Madison when give money. How you feel at time? You feel pity for Miss Madison, no? All other people also feel pity for Miss Madison, too."

I agreed that this was so.

"People not understand about learning," he went on. "Think necessary talk all time, that learn through mind, through words. Not so. Many things can only learn with feeling, even from sensation. But because man talk all time—use only formulatory centre—people not understand this. What you not see other night in study-house is that Miss Madison have new experience for her. Is poor woman, people not like, people think she funny—they laugh at. But other night, people not laugh. True, Miss Madison feel uncomfortable, feel embarrassed when I give money, feel shame perhaps. But when many people also feel for her sympathy, pity, compassion, even love, she understand this but not right away with mind. She feel, for first time in life, sympathy from many people. She not even know then that she feel this, but her life change; with you, I use you like example, last summer you hate Miss Madison. Now you not hate, you not think funny, you feel sorry. You even like Miss Madison. This good for her even if she not know right away—you will show; you cannot hide this from her, even if wish, cannot hide. So she now have friend, when used to be enemy. This good thing which I do for Miss Madison. I not concerned she understand this now—someday she understand and make her feel warm in heart. This unusual experience—this warm feeling—for such personality as Miss Madison who not have charm, who not friendly in self. Someday, perhaps even soon, she have good feeling because many people feel sorry, feel compassion for her. Someday she even understand what I do and even like me for this. But this kind learning take long time."

I understood him completely and was very moved by his words. But he had not finished.

"Also good thing for you in this," he said. "You young, only boy still, you not care about other people, care for self. I do this to Miss Madison and you think I do bad thing. You feel sorry, you not forget, you think I do bad thing to her. But now you understand not so. Also, good for you, because you feel about other person—you identify with Miss Madison, put self in her place, also regret what you do. Is necessary put self in place of other person if wish understand and help. This good for your conscience, this way is possibility for you learn not hate Miss Madison. All people same—stupid, blind, human. If I do bad thing, this make you learn love other people, not just self."

XV

GURDJIEFF'S TRIP TO the United States had been made, according to him, for various reasons—one of the most important ones being to make enough money to keep the Institute going at the Prieuré. Mr. Gurdjieff did not own the property, but rented it on a long-term lease, and since very few of the students were "paying guests", money was needed to make the various rental payments as well as to provide the food that we were unable to grow or produce on the land; to pay the light and gas and coal bills. And Mr. Gurdjieff's own expenses were also heavy at that time: he maintained an apartment in Paris, and had had to pay for the passage of all the students he had taken to America with him—enough, for instance, to be able to put on a demonstration of his gymnastics while he was there.

On his return, he frequently regaled us with stories about his adventures in America, about the American habit of embracing with open arms any new "movement", "theory", or "philosophy", simply in order to divert themselves, and about their gullibility in general. He would tell us how it was almost impossible for them not to give him money—the very act of giving him money made them feel important, and he called this "extortion" of them "shearing sheep". He said that most of them had pockets that were so full of green folding "stuff" that it gave them itchy fingers and they could not wait to part with it. Nevertheless, in spite of his stories about them and the way he made fun of them, he genuinely liked the Americans and, on occasions when he was not making fun of them, he would point out that, of all the peoples of the Western World, they were distinguished by various characteristics: their energy, ingenuity and their real generosity. Also, though gullible, they were good-hearted and eager to learn. Whatever their attributes or their faults, he had managed, during his stay in America, to collect a very large sum of money. I doubt that any one of us knew exactly how much, but it was generally believed to be in excess of $100,000.00.

The first obvious show of spending after his return to France was the sudden and unexpected delivery of literally scores of bicycles to the Prieuré. They arrived by the truckload, and Gurdjieff personally distributed them to everyone there, with only a very few exceptions: himself, his wife, and one or two of the smallest children. We were all amazed, and a great many of the Americans were appalled at this seeming waste of the money which many of them had helped to contribute to his "cause". Whatever his reasons for the acquisition of bicycles, the results were shatteringly colourful.

There were incredibly few people, considering the number of students living at the Prieuré at the time, who could actually ride a bicycle. But they had not been purchased idly—they were to be ridden. The entire grounds became a sort of enormous training-ground for bicycle riders. For days, and in the case of many of us, weeks, the grounds rang with the sound of bicycle bells, crashes, shouts of laughter and pain. In large groups we rode, teetering and collapsing to our assigned work on projects in the gardens and the woodlands. Anyone who had some valid reason or excuse for walking soon learned to beware of what had formerly been footpaths; for like as not, a bicycle would come careering at them, its rider frozen in horror and totally out of control, as he or she crashed into the unfortunate pedestrian or another equally helpless rider.

I suppose that most of us learned to ride quickly enough, although I seem to remember having bruised knees and elbows most of the summer. However long the process actually took, it seemed a very long time before it was safe to either ride or walk in the Prieuré grounds without genuine danger from almost any angle in the form of some novice bicyclist.

Another project that was initiated that same summer was equally colourful, although it did not involve the spending of any great sums of money. Everyone, with the sole exception of a skeleton group who had to work in the kitchen or on duty at the concierge, was put to work on the re-making of the lawns— the same lawns that I had mowed so arduously that first summer. No one escaped this duty, not even those so-called "distinguished" guests: persons who came for short visits, presumably to discuss Mr. Gurdjieff's theories with him, and who, up to that time, had not participated in work projects. Every available tool was put to use and the lawns were littered with people digging up the grass, raking, re-seeding, and rolling the new seed into the ground with heavy iron rollers. People worked so closely together that it sometimes seemed as if there was barely room for them all. During this activity, Gurdjieff would march up and down among all the workers, criticizing them individually, goading them on, and helping to contribute a feeling of furious, senseless activity to the whole proceedings. As one of the more recent American students remarked, surveying this ant-like activity, it was as if the entire student body, and perhaps particularly Gurdjieff, had at least temporarily taken leave of their senses.

At intervals, and sometimes for several hours at a time, Gurdjieff would suddenly cease his supervision of us, and go to sit at his small table from which he could watch all of us, and write steadily on his books. This only added to the comical aspect of the whole project.

It was on the second or third day that one voice rose in protest against the whole project. It was Rachmilevitch. In a towering rage, he laid down whatever implement he had been using, marched straight up to Gurdjieff and told him that what we were doing was insane. There were so many people working on the lawns, according to him, that the new grass-seed might better be thrown away than sown under our feet. People were digging and raking aimlessly, wherever they could find a vacant spot, paying no attention to what they were doing.

In what seemed to be equal fury, Gurdjieff protested against this uncalled for criticism—he knew better than anyone in the world how to "rebuild" lawns, he was an expert, he was not to be criticized, and so on, ad infinitum. After several minutes of this raging argument, Rachmilevitch turned on his heels and strode away. Everyone—we had all been impressed with his standing up to the "master" in this way—stopped their work and watched him until he disappeared into the woods beyond the furthest lawns.

It was not until an hour or so later, when we were about to pause for our usual afternoon tea, that Mr. Gurdjieff called me over to him. At some length he told me that it was essential that Mr. Rachmilevitch be found and brought back. He said that in order to save Rachmilevitch's face it was necessary to send for him, that he would never return of his own accord, and he instructed me to harness the horse and go and find him. When I protested that I did not even know where to begin to look, he said that he was sure that if I followed my own instincts I would locate him without difficulty and that, perhaps, even the horse would help.

In an attempt to put myself in Rachmilevitch's place, when I had harnessed the horse to the wagon, I set off towards the woods beyond the main, formal gardens. It seemed to me that he could only have gone to one of the distant vegetable gardens—a walk of at least a mile, and I headed for the furthest one, at the very end of the property. On the way I was troubled about what I would do if and when I did find him, particularly since I had been the chief culprit in the conspiracy against him during the winter. Nothing had ever been said about that to me—at least not by Gurdjieff—and I felt that I had been selected only because I was in charge of the horse, and that Gurdjieff could not have picked any less suitable candidate for this errand.

I was not very surprised when my hunch proved to be right. He was in the garden, as I had hoped he might be. But, as if to lend a dreamlike quality to the affair, he was not in what I would have thought a normal, usual place. He was, of all things, sitting up in an apple tree. Concealing my astonishment—I really did think he was mad—I drove the horse and wagon directly underneath the tree and stated my errand. He looked at me distantly and refused to go back. I did not know of any arguments—I could not think of any good reasons—with which to persuade him to come back, so I said that I would wait there as long as he did; that I could not return without him. After a long silence, during which he occasionally glared at me, he suddenly, without a word, dropped quietly into the wagon from the tree and then sat on the seat next to me as I drove back to the main house. Tea had been saved for us and we sat across from each other at the table as we drank our tea, while Gurdjieff watched us from a distant table. Everyone else had gone back to work.

When we had finished, Gurdjieff told me to unharness the horse, thanked me for finding Rachmilevitch, and said that he would see me later.

Gurdjieff came to the stable before I was through with the horse and asked me to tell him exactly where I had found Mr. Rachmilevitch. When I told him that I had found him sitting in a tree in the "far garden" he looked at me, incredulous, made me repeat this—asked me if I was absolutely sure—and I assured him that he had been in a tree and that I had had to sit there for a long time, under the tree, before he had consented to come back with me. He asked me what arguments I had used and I confessed that I had not been able to think of anything except to say that he had to come back and that I had said I would wait there for as long as he would. Gurdjieff seemed to find this whole story very amusing and thanked me profusely for telling it to him.

Poor Mr. Rachmilevitch. When everyone was assembled in the salon that evening, he was still an object of interest to us all. It was the first time that any of us could remember one single individual defying Gurdjieff in the presence of everyone else. But the incident was not over. After the customary playing of music on the piano by M. de Hartmann, Mr. Gurdjieff told us that he had a very amusing story to tell us, and proceeded to reconstruct, in elaborate details, and with a great many new embellishments of his own, the story of Rachmilevitch's defiance of the afternoon, his disappearance, and my "capture" of him. Not only was the story highly embellished, but he also acted out all the parts—himself, Rachmilevitch, the interested spectators, myself, even the horse. Amusing as it was to all of us, it was more than Rachmilevitch could bear. For the second time that day, he strode away from Gurdjieff after a furious outburst, vowing that he would leave the Prieuré for ever; he had, finally, had enough.

I do not believe that anyone took him seriously at the time, but, to our surprise and consternation, he actually did leave the following day for Paris. He had been so much a part of the place, so conspicuous because of his never-ending complaints, that it was like the end of an era—as if some essential property of the school had suddenly vanished.

XVI

JANE HEAP HAD returned to France at the same time as Gurdjieff, and had, of course, been to the Prieuré to see us. With her return, and to my regret, the visits to Paris to see Gertrude Stein and Alice Toklas had come to an end. I was very surprised when I was sent for one afternoon by the concierge, and told that I had a visitor. I was very pleased to learn that it was Gertrude and was very happy to see her, but my happiness was dispelled almost at once. Gertrude took a short walk with me in the grounds of the school, gave me a box of candy which she told me was a "farewell" gift for both of us from herself and Alice. She did not give me any opportunity to remonstrate with her, and said that she had made the trip to Fontainebleau especially to see us (I do not remember now whether she actually saw Tom or not) because she did not want to part from us by simply writing a letter.

When I asked her what she meant, she said that because of some difficulty she was having with Jane, and also because she still thought that we were not being properly brought up, she had decided that she could no longer go on seeing us. Any relationship with her, because of her disagreement with Jane— and, I gathered, with Gurdjieff as well—would inevitably only make trouble for us. There was nothing that I could say to this. Gertrude cut my protests short, said that she was very sorry to have to do what she was doing, but that there was no other way out.

I was shocked and saddened by this sudden, unexpected end to what had been a very happy, exciting and rewarding relationship, and, perhaps mistakenly, I think I blamed Jane for it. I cannot remember whether I ever mentioned it to Jane, or whether she explained it to me, but I do remember feeling, perhaps mistakenly, that she—not Gurdjieff—was the cause. Whatever the cause, my relationship with Jane deteriorated steadily from that time on, and while she was still my legal guardian, I rarely saw her. Looking back on my behaviour at that time, it now seems to me that I was being uncivilized to a high degree—I don't know about Jane. Jane made her usual periodic visits to the Prieuré on weekends but while I actually did see her—that is, I saw her with my eyes from a distance—we hardly spoke to each other for a period of about two years. She did, of course, see Tom and Gurdjieff, and I knew from the general gossip at the school and from Tom that the "problem of Fritz" was frequently discussed and also that Gurdjieff had been brought into these discussions; however, during that entire time, when I was still in very close contact with Gurdjieff because of my room-cleaning duties, he never mentioned Jane to me, and his behaviour towards me never altered. Not only did it not alter, but, partly because of the break with Jane, my feelings of respect and love for him only increased.

When Gurdjieff returned from his first trip to Paris after the "Rachmilevitch affair", to our surprise, he brought Rachmilevitch back with him. In the short period that he had been absent from the Prieuré he seemed to have changed a great deal. He now appeared to be resigned instead of contentious and quarrelsome, and in the course of time we even began to feel a certain affection for him. I was very curious about his return and while I did not have the temerity to bring up the subject directly when I was with Gurdjieff, he brought it up himself. He simply asked me, unexpectedly, if I were not surprised to see Rachmilevitch back at the Prieuré, and I told him that I was very surprised and admitted that I was, also, curious as to how it had happened; his resolve to leave for ever had been very definite.

Gurdjieff then told me the story of Rachmilevitch. According to this tale, Rachmilevitch had been a Russian refugee who had located in Paris after the Russian revolution and had become a prosperous merchant dealing in such merchandise as teas, caviar, and various other products for which there was, primarily, a demand among displaced Russian persons. Gurdjieff had apparently known him for a long time—he may have been one of the people who came to France with Gurdjieff from Russia some years before—and had decided that his personality was an essential element in the school.

"You remember," he said, "how I tell you that you make trouble? This true, but you only child. Rachmilevitch grown man and not mischievous, like you, but have such personality that he constantly cause friction whatever he do, wherever he live. He not make serious trouble, but he make friction on surface of life, all the time. He cannot help this—he too old to change now.

"When I tell you that though Rachmilevitch is already rich merchant I pay him to stay here, you are surprised, but this so. He very old friend and very important for my purposes. I cannot pay him what he can already make, all by self, in tea business in Paris; so when I go to see him I humble self, have to beg him to make sacrifice for my sake. He agree to do this, and I now have obligation to him for life. Without Rachmilevitch, Prieuré is not same; I know no one person like him, no person who just by existence, without conscious effort, produce friction in all people around him."

I had by this time acquired the habit of always assuming that in anything that Gurdjieff did there was always "more than meets the eye"; I was also familiar with his theory that friction produced conflicts which, in turn, agitated people and, as it were, shocked them out of their habitual, routine behaviour; also I could not help but wonder what rewards were in this for Rachmilevitch, besides money, that is. Gurdjieff's only answer to this was to say that it was also a privilege for Rachmilevitch to be at the Prieuré. "Nowhere else can his personality perform such useful work." I was not particularly impressed by this answer, but I did have a picture in my mind of Rachmilevitch's every move being of great importance. It seemed, at best, a curious destiny—he must, I assumed, live in a constant state of cataclysm, creating havoc incessantly.

There was no question that his presence not only created trouble, but also seemed to attract it. Very shortly after his return, he and I were again the focal points in another "incident".

It was my day on kitchen duty. As was customary for the "kitchen-boy" I got up at four-thirty in the morning. Since I was lazy by nature and also at that age, the only way I could be sure of awakening on time for kitchen duty was to drink as many glasses of water as I could before I went to bed at about eleven the night before. Alarm clocks were unheard of at the Prieuré, and this recipe for early rising (which someone had suggested to me) never failed to work. As the nearest toilet was at a considerable distance from my room, there was no doubt of my actual waking up and I did not fall asleep again. The only difficulty was in regulating the amount of water. Too often I awakened at three, instead of four-thirty. Even on those mornings I did not dare to go back to bed again, and could not face drinking another quantity of water sufficient to waken me in another hour or so.

The kitchen boy's first duties were to build the fires in the coke stoves, fill the coal scuttles, make the coffee and heat the milk, slice and toast the bread. The water for the coffee took a long time to come to a boil as it was heated in twenty-five litre enamelware pots, which were also used to make the soup for the midday meal. The cook—there was usually a different cook every day, but the menus were written down, with recipes, in advance for each day of the week—normally was not required to appear in the kitchen until breakfast was over. On this particular day, the cook had not appeared by nine-thirty and I began to worry. I looked at the menu, and the recipe for the soup of the day, and since I had often seen the various cooks prepare the meal that was scheduled for that day, I made the necessary preliminary preparations.

When the cook had still not appeared by about ten o'clock I sent some child to find out what had happened to her and was told that she was sick and would not be able to come to the kitchen. I took my dilemma to Gurdjieff, and he said that since I had already started the meal I might as well return to the kitchen and finish it. "You be cook today," he said grandly.

I was very nervous about the responsibility, as well as rather proud of being entrusted with it. My greatest difficulty was in having to move the enormous soup kettles around the top of the large coal stove when I had to add coal to the fire, which was frequently necessary in order to keep the soup cooking. I worked hard all the morning and was reasonably proud of myself when I managed to finish the meal and deliver it, intact, to the serving table. The cook being absent, it was also necessary for me to serve it.

Habitually, the students formed a line, each person with his soup plate, silver, etc., in his hands, and as they passed by the serving table the cook would serve them one piece of meat and a ladleful of soup. Everything went well for a time. It was not until Rachmilevitch appeared—among the last to be served—that my difficulties began. The soup pot was almost empty by the time he reached me and I had to tilt it in order to fill the ladle. When I served him—it seemed to me that it was decreed by our mutual fates—the ladle also brought up a fair-sized lump of coke. It was a thick soup and I did not see the coke until it was deposited, with a hard, clanking sound, in his soup plate.

Judging by Rachmilevitch's reaction, his world came to an end at that instant. He started in on a tirade against me that I thought would never end. Everything that all of the children had done to him during the past winter was brought up, hashed over in detail; and as he cursed and raged I stood helplessly behind the soup kettle, silent. The tirade came to an end with Gurdjieff's appearance. He did not usually appear at lunch—he did not eat lunch—and he explained his appearance by saying that we were making so much noise that he was unable to work.

Rachmilevitch turned on him immediately, beginning his recital of woes and wrongs all over again from the beginning. Gurdjieff watched him steadily, unblinking, and this seemed to have a calming effect. Rachmilevitch's voice gradually lowered in tone, and he seemed to run down. Without saying anything to him, Gurdjieff picked the lump of coke out of Rachmilevitch's soup plate, threw it on the ground, and asked for a plate of soup himself. He said that since there was a new cook today, he felt that it was his responsibility to taste his cooking. Someone went for a soup plate for him, I served him what remained in the soup pot and he ate it, silently. When he had finished, he came over to me, congratulated me loudly, and said that the soup—this particular soup—was a favourite of his and was better than he had ever tasted.

He then turned to the assembled students and said that he had great experience and training in many things, and that in the course of his life he had learned a great deal about food, chemistry, and proper cooking, which included, of course, the taste of things. He said that while this particular soup was one that he had, personally, invented and which he liked very much, he now realized that it had always lacked one element to make it perfect. With a sort of obeisance in my direction, he praised me saying that I, by a fortunate accident, had found the perfect thing—the one thing that this soup needed. Carbon. He ended this speech by saying that he would instruct his secretary to change the recipe to include one piece of coke— not to be eaten, but to be added for flavour only. He then invited Rachmilevitch to have after-dinner coffee with him, and they left the dining area together.

XVII

ALTHOUGH THERE WERE many people at the Prieuré who were considered important for one reason or another, such as Madame de Hartmann, his secretary, and her husband, the pianist and composer, M. de Hartmann, who arranged and played the various pieces of music which Gurdjieff composed on his small "harmonium", the most impressive permanent resident was his wife, who was always known to us as Madame Ostrovsky.

She was a very tall, big-boned, handsome woman, and she seemed to be ever-present, moving almost silently along the corridors of the buildings, supervising the operation of the kitchens, the laundry-rooms and the general housekeeping work. I never knew exactly how much, or what, authority she had. On the few occasions when she actually said anything to us, which were rare, there was no question in our minds but that her word was law. I remember being particularly fascinated by the way she moved; she walked without any perceptible movement of her head and without the slightest jerkiness in her movements; she was never hurried, but at the same time she worked at incredible speed; every movement she made in whatever she was doing was absolutely essential to that particular activity. During the first summer at the Prieuré she usually prepared Gurdjieff's meals and took them to his room, and it was when she was in the kitchen that we had an opportunity to observe her at work. She rarely spoke, in fact, she did not seem to use words as a means of communication unless it was absolutely essential, and when she did speak, she never raised her voice. She seemed surrounded by an aura of gentle firmness; everyone regarded her with a certain awe, and she inspired a very real feeling of devotion, although it was hardly ever expressed outwardly, among all the children.

Although most of us had no contact with her in the usual sense—for example, I doubt that she ever even addressed me personally—when we learned that she was seriously ill, it was a matter of concern to all of us. We missed the feeling of unspoken authority that she had always carried with her, and the lack of her presence gave us a feeling of definite, if indefinable, loss.

Her illness, in addition, made a great change in Gurdjieff's routine. Once she was confined to her room—which faced his room and was of equal size, but at the opposite end of the main building—Gurdjieff began to spend several hours with her each day. He would go to her room for a short visit each morning, supervise the persons who were delegated to taking care of her—his two eldest nieces and, on occasion, others—and would then return after lunch, usually to spend the entire afternoon with her.

During this period, our contact with Gurdjieff was rare, except for the evenings in the salon. He was preoccupied and withdrawn and left almost all of the details of the running of the Prieuré to others. We occasionally saw him when we were on kitchen duty as he would come to the kitchens to supervise, personally, the preparation of her food. She was on a diet which included a large amount of blood, pressed in a small hand press from meat which had been especially selected and purchased for her.

At the beginning of her illness, she did make occasional appearances on the terrace, to sit in the sun, but as the summer went on she finally took to her room permanently. Gurdjieff informed us, one evening, that she was incurably ill with some form of cancer and that the doctors—some two months before—had given her only two weeks to live. He said that although it might take all his strength, he was determined to keep her alive for as long as possible. He said that she was "living through him" and that it took almost all of his daily energy, but that he hoped to keep her alive for another year, or at least for six months.

As I was still in charge of his rooms, I necessarily had a certain amount of contact with him. He would often send for coffee during the night, which was now the only time he gave to his writing—often staying up until four or five in the morning, having worked from about ten o'clock the night before.

In addition to the chickens, the donkey, the horse, a number of sheep, and for a time one cow, there were a number of cats and dogs around the Prieuré. One of the dogs, a rather ugly black and white mongrel, had always tended to follow Gurdjieff around, but not to such an extent that he could have been called Gurdjieff's dog. At this period, with Gurdjieff rarely absent from the Prieuré—he had cut his trips to Paris to an absolute minimum—this dog, named Philos by Gurdjieff, became his constant companion. He not only followed him everywhere, but also slept in Gurdjieff's room unless Gurdjieff put him out personally, which he usually did, telling me that he did not like anyone or anything sleeping in the same room with him. Upon being put out of the room, Philos would curl up directly in front of the door, and then go to sleep against it. He was a reasonably fierce watchdog and became very protective of Gurdjieff. He was, however, extremely tolerant of me as I was—obviously with Gurdjieff's permission—constantly coming and going to and from Gurdjieff's room. When I would enter it late at night with my tray of coffee, he would glare up at me, yawn and permit me to step over him and enter the room.

One night, it was very late and the entire Prieuré was silent and dark with the exception of Gurdjieff's room, Gurdjieff set aside his work when I came in and told me to sit on the bed beside him. He talked at some length about his work, how hard his writing was, how exhausting his daily work with Madame Ostrovsky, and then, as usual, asked me about myself. I recapitulated the various things that I was doing, and he commented that since I had a great deal to do with animals—I took care of the chickens, the horse, the donkey, and recently had been feeding Philos, too—he would like to know what I thought of them. I said that I thought of them all as my friends and told him, to his amusement, that I even had names for all the chickens.

He said that the chickens were not important—very stupid creatures—but that he hoped that I would take good care of the other animals. The donkey did not matter too much, but he was concerned with the horse and the dogs. "Horse and dog, and sometimes also true of cow," he said, "are special animals. Can do many things with such animals. In America, in Western world, people make fools of dogs—make learn tricks, other stupid things. But these animals truly special—no longer just animals." He then asked me if I had ever heard of reincarnation and I said that I had. He said that there were people, some Buddhists for example, who had many theories about reincarnation, some "even believe animal can become man— or sometimes that man in next reincarnation can become animal." He laughed when he said this, and then added: "Man do many strange things with religion when learn a little—make up new things for religion, sometimes things that have little truth, but usually come from original thing that was true. In case of dogs, they not all wrong," he said. "Animals have only two centres—man is three-centred being, with body, heart, and mind, all different. Animal cannot acquire third brain and become man; but just because of this, because of this impossibility to acquire third brain, is necessary always treat animals with kindness. You know this word, 'kindness'?"

I said that I did, and he said: "Never forget this word. Very good word and not exist in many languages. Not in French, for instance. French say 'gentil' but this not mean same thing. Not *kind*, kind come from kin, like family, like same thing. Kindness mean to treat like self."

"Reason for necessity treat dog and horse with kindness," he went on, "is because unlike all other animal, and even though he know cannot become man, cannot acquire third brain like man, in his heart all dog and horse who associate with man *wish* become man. You look at dog or horse and you always see, in eyes, this sadness because know not possible for them, but even so, they wish. This very sad thing to wish for impossible. They wish this because of man. Man corrupts such animals, man almost try to make dog and horse human. You have heard people say 'my dog almost like human'—they not know they speak near-truth when say this, because is almost truth, but still impossible. Dog and horse seem like human because have this wish. So, Freets,"—as he always pronounced my name—"you remember this important thing. Take good care of animals; always be kind."

He then spoke about Madame Ostrovsky. He said that his work with her was extremely tiring and very difficult "because I try to do thing with her which almost not possible. If she alone, already she be long time dead. I keep alive, make stay alive, with my strength; very difficult thing. But also very important—this most important moment in life for her. She live many lives, is very old soul; she now have possibility ascend to other world. But sickness come and make more difficult, make impossible for her do this thing alone. If can keep alive few months more will not have to come back and live this life again. You now part of Prieuré family—my family—you can help by making strong wish for her, not for long life, but for proper death at right time. Wish can help, is like prayer when for other. When for self, prayer and wish no good; only work good for self. But when wish with heart for other, can help."

When he had finished, he looked at me for a long time, patted my head in that affectionate animal way, and sent me to bed.

XVIII

ALTHOUGH GURDJIEFF WAS always set apart from everyone else at the Prieuré, unquestioned, and accorded great respect which was combined with a proper element of fear, his "dictatorship" was also very benevolent. There was a side of his nature that was not only physically magnetic and animal-like, but extremely earthy. His sense of humour was often very subtle, in an oriental sense, but also had a broad, crude side, and he was a very sensual man.

He manifested this side of himself particularly when he was alone with the men and boys—in the Turkish bath or, during the summer, at the swimming pool. Our swimming pool was at the far end of the formal lawns and gardens, facing the château beyond the expanse of lawns. Contrary to popular belief, there was no mingling of the sexes in any "immoral" sense. The men and women bathed separately at the bath, and different hours were allotted for male or female use of the swimming pool. There was, in fact, a very strict code of morality in this purely physical sense, and we were highly amused when people sent us clippings from the Sunday supplements of various newspapers which "proved" that the Institute was a nudist colony, or a "free-love" group—some sort of crack-pot organization tinged with a certain licentiousness. Actually the nearest thing to "nudity" was the common habit—for some of the men only, of course—of working out of doors stripped to the waist. And, while it was true that we swam without bathing suits, the swimming pool was equipped with curtains which were always drawn whenever anyone went in swimming. It was forbidden, in fact, for even the small children to swim without drawing the curtains.

In spite of Gurdjieff's many preoccupations—especially his wife's illness—that summer, he frequently joined the other men and the boys at their allotted hour before lunch at the swimming pool. When everyone had stripped, Gurdjieff would, inevitably, begin to joke about their bodies, their sexual prowess, their various physical habits. The jokes were usually what would be called "dirty" or at least "lewd" and he found all such stories highly amusing, whether he told them or whether they were told by the other men who were quick to join in the spirit of such joking. One of his favourite amusements or diversions at the swimming pool was to line all the men up facing in one direction and then compare their sunburns. This became a ritual of what Gurdjieff called the "white ass" club. He would look at all of us from the rear, remarking on the various shades of tan or sunburn, and the glowing whiteness of our buttocks. He would then make us all turn around and make additional comments on the size and variety of male genitalia exposed to him. Finally, we would, each time he appeared to swim, be rated, as members in good standing of his "white ass" club. Tom and I usually rated high—in addition to deeply tanned backs and chests, since we were children and wore shorts, our legs were also deeply tanned, and because of this he would make some comment, usually to the effect that our small buttocks were "asses that shine with whiteness, like stars."

A good many of the older men, particularly the Russians, not only did not expose themselves to the sun, but rather disliked any form of nudity and were usually embarrassed by these proceedings. They, of course, rated very low on the list, but Gurdjieff, himself, was the lowest. So low, as he said, that he actually belonged to a different club. Since he always wore a hat—winter and summer—although his face was dark, his bald head was a glistening white. His club, of which he was the president and sole member, was called something like the "white crown" club, and he would compare the whiteness of his bald pate with the whiteness—he made elaborate comparisons of the degree of white always—of our behinds.

One of his favourite stories on these occasions was a long, involved tale about a farmhand who was having an affair with the farmer's wife. The farmer, suspecting his wife and the farmhand, went searching for them with his rifle, and discovered them when he perceived, in the moonlight, the farmhand's white ass, bouncing rhythmically through the darkness, shining in the reflected light of the moon. Although these stories were often repeated and many of them were not, in the first place, particularly funny, his own immense enjoyment in telling them made us all laugh. He was a superb story-teller, spinning out even the dullest tales to such fantastic lengths, embellishing them with such ornamention and detail, accompanied by pointed, significant gestures and expressions, that it was impossible not to listen to him with total absorption.

The subtler side of his humour—which was always complicated and involved—expressed itself very differently. Early that summer, a group of us, for our own amusement, had been exploring the cellars of the main building and we had come across a tunnel. While we did follow it for almost half a mile, the rats, cobwebs, and mouldy dankness, and the complete darkness, kept us from trying to reach its end. There was a rumour that, since the Prieuré had been reputedly built by Louis XIV for Madame de Maintenon, this was an underground passage to the Palace of Fontainebleau. Be that as it may, Gurdjieff was greatly interested in our discovery of this tunnel, and went to examine it personally.

A week or so after this discovery, he told me that he had an important job for me. He talked at some length about the tunnel, and then asked me to take a bottle of the ordinary red wine which we drank at meals, and bought at that time for about eight cents a litre, open it, pour out half of it and then refill the bottle by the addition of half a bottle of sparkling Perrier water. I was then to recork the bottle, seal it with sealing wax, cover it with sand and cobwebs—"wonderful cobwebs for this purpose in tunnel"—and bring it to him when he called for it.

I must have looked puzzled, and he went on to explain that two very distinguished guests were scheduled to visit him the following week. This wine was being prepared especially for them. He would call me and when he asked for "one of the bottles of the special old wine" I was to bring this bottle with a cork-screw and two glasses. He smiled a good deal during these instructions and I made no comment about them, although I knew that he was "up to something"—a phrase he often used when he was planning anything.

The two visitors arrived. They were well-known to me, in fact they were well-known, by reputation, to everyone there, and they elicited the automatic admiration and respect that is generally accorded to "famous" people, whether actually deserved or not. I ushered the visitors—both women—to Gurdjieff's room and then retired to my waiting post near the bell (there were two bells for me—one in the kitchen and one in my room). When I heard the expected ring I ran to his room and was told to bring "the special old, rare wine that we had found during a recent project of excavating the ruins of the original monastery". This colourful exaggeration had a basis in fact. The Prieuré had been, in the 12th century, a monastery and there were a few ruins to substantiate this. Those ruins, of course, had nothing at all to do with the tunnel from the cellars. The original monastery building had been at a completely different location on the property.

I brought the wine as I had been instructed with only two glasses, the bottle completely covered with dirt, sand and cobwebs, plus a napkin with which to hold it—my personal touch of elegance. Before telling me to open the bottle (he simply told me to wait there for a few minutes) he told them the story of the wine that was about to be served.

He began with a long, and highly inaccurate, account of the founding of the Prieuré (in 900) by some order of monks who, among other things, like all monks, made wine. "These special monks; very intelligent. Monks like this no longer exist on earth. With such intelligence," he continued, "naturally such monk make also very wonderful wine."

He then said, with a quick, stern glance at me, as if to silence any possible laughter from me, "I have many projects, all very important, at Prieuré. One project this year is excavation of old ruins." He then described, at great length, the number of people and the great energy involved in this project and how, miraculously, we had come across eleven bottles of wine . . . wine that had been made by these self-same intelligent monks. "Now come problem for me . . . who I know worthy to drink such wine; wine that no longer exist anywhere in world except here at Prieuré? This wine too good for me. I already ruin stomach with drinking Armagnac. Then I think of just you ladies, who, as if by Act of God, plan to visit me. Just most suitable ladies to first taste this wine."

I was then ordered to open the bottle. I wrapped it in the napkin, uncorked it and poured a little of the "wine" into the two glasses. Gurdjieff watched me with great intensity, and when I passed the wine to the two ladies, he turned his equally intense attention to them; he appeared to be burning with anticipation, unable to wait for their reaction.

The ladies, properly impressed and suiting their actions to the momentous occasion, lifted their glasses gingerly in his direction and sipped, delicately. Gurdjieff was unable to restrain himself. "Tell!" he commanded them. "How taste this wine?"

The ladies, as if overcome, were momentarily unable to speak. At last, one of them, with half-closed eyes, murmured that it was "superb"; the other adding that she had never tasted anything to compare with it.

Puzzled, and embarrassed on their account, I started to leave the room but Gurdjieff stopped me with a firm gesture and indicated that I was to refill their glasses. I stayed with them until they had finished the bottle, with continued appropriate exclamations of rapture and ecstasy. He then told me to take the bottle and glasses, to prepare their rooms—on the very same floor as his—one room in which Napoleon had slept, the other having been occupied at some point by some King's mistress—and to let him know when the rooms were ready.

The rooms, of course, had been ready that morning, but I laid fires in the fireplaces, waited a suitable time and then returned to his room. He told me to take them to their rooms, and then instructed them that they must rest after the experience of having tasted this marvellous wine, and must prepare for the feast of the evening—a great feast which was being prepared, especially in their honour.

When I saw him later, alone, his only mention of the wine-drinking episode was to congratulate me on the appearance of the bottle. I gave him a significant, knowing look as if to tell him that I had understood what he was doing, and he said, rather seriously, but with a faint, mocking smile on his face: "Way you look, I know you already make judgment of this ladies; but remember what I tell before, necessary look all sides, all directions before make judgment. You not forget this."

XIX

I SOMETIMES THOUGHT of Gurdjieff as a clever fisherman or trapper; the incident of the ladies and the "famous old wine" was only one of many instances in which he, to my mind at least, laid a trap or baited a hook and then sat back to watch, with great amusement, the prey reveal themselves, their weaknesses, when caught. Although I sensed an element of malice in this, the saving grace seemed to lie in the fact that, in most cases, the "prey" was unaware of what had happened. At times, it seemed to me that this kind of "playing" with people was literally nothing more than a diversion for him, something to take his mind off the continuous pressures under which he worked. When speaking of such experiences, he would frequently refer to them as "bubble-pricking", which I did not find especially apt since the "deflating" was frequently unnoticed by the particular target of the moment.

In the normal course of time, Gurdjieff acquired numerous reputations, including that of a sort of "faith-healer" or, on a somewhat simpler level, "miracle-worker". It was perhaps inevitable that he was, therefore, frequently consulted about day-to-day "life" or "mundane" problems, in spite of the fact that he had frequently reiterated that his work had nothing to do with the solution of such problems. Nevertheless, and even though forewarned, a great many people insisted on consulting him about just such problems, which seemed to me surprising and, usually, embarrassing, particularly since the people who did consult him were generally considered, or at least considered themselves, intellectual, intelligent people.

I remember one woman who, at great expense to herself (which was perhaps not pertinent, since she had money), made a trip from America to the Prieuré, for one week, to consult him about the very kind of problem which he had so often stated was not in his province. When she arrived, she demanded an immediate interview, but was told that Gurdjieff would be unable to see her until sometime that evening. She was assigned to a comfortable room and, through his secretary, told that she would have to pay a large sum, daily, for the use of the room. She was also warned that there would be an additional, large fee for her "consultation".

He did not see her alone, but met and welcomed her at dinner that evening in the presence of everyone. In the course of his preliminary conversation with her, he said that he understood she had an important problem to discuss with him, and he behaved as if he were enormously impressed that she should have made such a long, expensive trip just to consult him. She said that the problem was one that had troubled her for a long time, and that she had felt—when she had met him in America the previous winter—that he was, unquestionably, the only person who could help her to solve it. He said that he would try to help her, and that she could make an appointment for an appropriate time for such a consultation by speaking to his secretary. She went on to say, in front of the entire assembled company, that it was very urgent. He said that he would see her as soon as possible but that, for now, the important business of the day was to have dinner.

At the dinner table, the woman gave every appearance of great nervousness, smoked one cigarette after another, and coughed a great deal—to such an extent that everyone at the table was aware of her. Giving up any attempt at conversation because of her constant coughing, Gurdjieff remarked that she seemed to have a bad cough. She responded at once, pleased with this attention, and said that it was part of the problem about which she wished to consult him. He frowned at her, but before he had an opportunity to say anything more, she plunged ahead. She said that she was having trouble with her husband and that her cigarette-smoking and her coughing were simply "exterior manifestations", in her opinion, of this difficulty. We were all listening (I was waiting on table) by this time. Gurdjieff frowned at her again, but she went on relentlessly. She said that cigarettes, as everyone knew, were a phallic symbol, and that she had discovered that her excessive smoking and the resultant coughing were "manifestations" which always occurred when she was having the aforesaid difficulty with her husband, adding that, of course, her troubles were sexual.

Gurdjieff had listened to her, as he always did, with undivided attention, and after a thoughtful pause he asked her what kind of cigarettes she smoked. She named an American brand which she said she had smoked for years. He nodded, very thoughtfully, at this disclosure, and after a suspenseful silence said that he thought the cure, or the solution, was very simple. He suggested that she change her brand of cigarettes, that perhaps "Gauloises Bleues" would be a good brand to try. For the time being that ended the conversation.

It was only later, in the salon, during the rather ceremonious coffee-drinking, that she was heard to praise him extravagantly and say that he had, of course, given her the solution—that his way of solving problems was never obvious, but that she had understood him.

She stayed at the Prieuré for a day or two longer, bought an enormous supply of "Gauloises Bleues"—as many as the law allowed her to take out of the country—and without demanding any further consultations, and having informed Gurdjieff that she had understood him, returned to America. It was only after her departure that Gurdjieff referred to her as "one of those God-given accidents who have unconscious good-will for me." He had charged her a large fee and she had paid it gladly.

Although I did not mention it to Mr. Gurdjieff at the time, I did refer to that incident and others like it, some time later. At that time, he told me that many people—people with "middle-class western world morality" had questions about, and objections to, his methods of procuring money, which he always needed for the support of the Prieuré and also of many of the students who were not able to pay him anything. He said, almost angrily, that our kind of morality was based on money; that the only thing that troubled us about such occurrences was the fact that he had, apparently, extracted money without having given anything in return.

"All my life," he said forcefully, "I tell people this work not for everyone. If can solve problems with religion or with your American psychiatrist, this good. But people not listen what I say; always find other meaning—interpret what I say in own way, make self feel good. So must pay for this good feeling. Many times I tell that my work cannot help with ordinary life problems: sex, illness, unhappiness; such things. If cannot solve such problems alone, then my work, which not have to do with such problems, no good for them. But such people come here no matter what I tell, to have good feeling; woman who smoke many cigarettes can now tell everyone, but particularly her 'self' that she consult me about problem and that I give answer, even though I not give answer. So just such people can justify existence by helping me with many money problems. Even with their stupidity they help good thing—my work. This already enough reward for such people.

"Is unfortunate weakness in people today; they ask advice but not wish help, wish only find what already want. They not listen words I say—I always say what I mean, my words always clear—but they not believe this, always look for other meaning, meaning which exist only in their imagination. Without such woman, such people, you and many other people at Prieuré not eat. Money this woman pay is money for food." It was one of the few times that I had ever heard him "explain" or "justify" such activity on his part.

XX

In the natural course of events, since Mr. Gurdjieff was engaged in writing books, it was necessary for him to employ a typist. He did not set about this in any ordinary manner, but he employed, with great fanfare, a young German woman he had discovered somewhere in his travels. For several days before her arrival we heard about her. Elaborate preparations were made for her coming, including finding the proper room for her, the acquisition of a typewriter, arrangements for suitable working space, and so on. Gurdjieff praised her attributes to all of us, told us how lucky he had been to find this perfect person "for my purposes", and we awaited her arrival with great anticipation.

When she did arrive, she was introduced to all of us, a dinner was served in her honour, and the whole process was very festive—she was given what we called the "royal treatment", and she responded to it whole-heartedly, taking herself as seriously as Gurdjieff seemed to take her. It turned out that her major, magnificent accomplishment was that she could type, as Gurdjieff repeatedly told us in complete amazement, "without even looking at key on typewriter."

No secretary or typist has, I feel sure, ever been accorded such treatment because of her ability to use the touch system. As if to prove to us all that this ability actually existed, the young woman installed herself at a table on the terrace, in full view of all of us as we came and went to and from our work, and remained there—typing merrily—all summer long, except on rainy days. The clicking of her typewriter resounded in all of our ears.

My first contact with her, and in fairness to her I must admit to a strong anti-German prejudice, having grown up on stories of German atrocities during World War I, was one evening when I was doing my own washing in the courtyard in back of the house after work. She did not know me, except by sight, and, assuming that I was French, called to me from a window overlooking the courtyard, asking me in heavily accented French where she could obtain what she called some

"Savon Lux"; she managed to convey to me that she needed this to wash her stockings. I said, in English, which I knew she understood and spoke much better than French, that I assumed she could buy it at the local *épicerie* about half a mile distant. Her response was to toss some coins down to me and to tell me that she would appreciate my getting her some at once.

I picked up the money, went up the stairs and handed it to her. I said that I thought I should explain to her that there were no errand boys at the Prieuré and that no one had, so far, told me that she was any exception to the general rule that everyone did their own personal work, which included personal shopping. She said, with a "charming" smile, that she was sure that no one would have any objection to my performing this errand for her since she was, as perhaps I did not yet realize, engaged on very important work for Mr. Gurdjieff. I explained that I, too, was engaged on similar work; that I took care of him and his rooms and did my own errands as well.

She seemed amazed, and after a moment's reflection said that she would straighten out the matter with Mr. Gurdjieff—that there must be some misunderstanding, at least on my part, concerning her function at the school. I did not have to wait very long for further developments. A "coffee summons" came from his room only a few minutes later.

When I arrived at his room with the coffee, the typist, as I had expected, was sitting with him. I served the coffee and then Mr. Gurdjieff turned to me with one of his "winning" smiles: "You know this lady?" he asked.

I said that, yes, I knew her.

He then said that she had spoken to him and that he understood that she had asked me to perform an errand for her and that I had refused. I said that it was true and that, besides, everyone else performed their own errands.

He agreed that this was so, but said that he had not had time to instruct her about everything and that he would appreciate it very much if, on this one occasion and as a favour to him, because she was very important to him, I would be kind enough to do what she asked. I was baffled and even angry, but I said, of course, that I would. She handed me the money and I went to the store and bought her soap. I assumed that, however I might feel, he had a good reason for asking me to do the errand for her and decided that the incident was closed. Perhaps she was actually "special" in some way that I had not realized; Gurdjieff, at least, appeared to think she was.

I was furious, however, when after I had given her the soap and her change, she gave me a tip and said that she was sure that I now realized that she had been right in the first place, and that she hoped Mr. Gurdjieff's action had made it clear to me. I smouldered, but managed to hold my tongue. I also managed not to mention it to Mr. Gurdjieff when I saw him, but I continued to smoulder.

Several days later, on a weekend, a number of guests arrived. Gurdjieff welcomed them at his usual little table near the lawns, in front of the terrace where the typist was at work. I brought coffee for all of them and served it. He indicated, with a gesture, that I was not to leave, and then proceeded to tell the assembled guests that he could hardly wait to show them his new marvels, his two wonderful new acquisitions: an electric icebox and a "touch typist". He then told me to lead the way to the pantry where the new refrigerator had been installed, and the guests were properly mystified upon being shown an ordinary model Frigidaire which, as Gurdjieff put it, "all by self can make ice", even, "without my help"— a true product of the genius of the western world. This inspection completed, we all went back to the terrace to inspect the second marvel who, also "without my help and even without looking at keys", was able to type his book. The typist stood up to greet him but Gurdjieff, without introducing her, told her to sit down. Then, at his command, she typed "without even looking at keys" but gazing triumphantly off into space.

Gurdjieff stood among his guests, gazing at her with unbounded admiration, speaking of her as another product of the "genius" of the western world. I was, actually, fascinated by the ability to use the touch system on a typewriter and my own interest and admiration were unfeigned. Gurdjieff, suddenly, looked in my direction and smiled an enormous, broad smile, as if we shared some huge joke together, and then told me to collect the coffee cups.

It was not until much later that evening, in his room, that he referred to the typist once more. He spoke first of the "electric icebox"—"only have to put in plug and instantly box make noise of humming and begin produce ice." He smiled at me again, conspiratorially. "Is so with German lady.

I like plug—I tell type, and she also begin make noise and produce not ice, but book. Wonderful American invention."

I almost liked her then, and would have been happy to do her errands from that time on. I could not refrain from saying so, and Gurdjieff nodded at me, looking pleased. "When you help typing lady, you help me, like giving oil to machine which keep working; this wonderful thing."

XXI

ONE OF THE pleasures and challenges of "concierge duty" was a competition among all the children—this duty was almost exclusively the work of the children—to be sufficiently alert on this job to have the gates, through which the automobiles had to pass, opened in time for Mr. Gurdjieff to drive through them without having to stop his car and blow the horn as a signal to the gatekeeper.

One difficulty with this was that the entrance to the Prieuré was at the foot of a long hill which descended from the railway station; the streetcar to Samois also passed directly in front of the gate where the highway made a wide turn in the direction of Samois, away from the Prieuré. Frequently the noise of the "tramway" obscured the sound of cars coming down the hill, and interfered with our game. Also, once Mr. Gurdjieff became aware of the competition, he would usually coast down the hill so that we would not be aided by the sound of the motor.

It was mostly thanks to Philos, the dog, who often followed me around during Mr. Gurdjieff's absences, that I was usually able to get the gates opened in time for him to sail through them, a big smile on his face. By watching Philos, whose ears would prick up at the sound of any passing car, but who would jump to his feet at the sound of Mr. Gurdjieff's car, I was almost always successful.

Amused by this game of ours, Mr. Gurdjieff once asked me how it was that I was able to, practically unfailingly, have the gates open in time, and I told him about Philos. He laughed and then said that this was a very good example of cooperation. "Show that man have much to learn, and can learn from many unexpected places. Even dog can help. Man very weak, need help all time."

Late that summer, I was on concierge duty when Mr. Gurdjieff was to leave on a trip. For some reason, it was a particularly important departure, and everyone was gathered around his automobile when he was about ready to leave. I was among the leave-takers, and when he had finally started the motor of the car, I ran to the big gates to open them. In my haste, I stumbled and fell, and one of my knees hit the heavy iron catch, just above the level of the ground, which served to hold one of the gates open. It was rusty and, as I had fallen hard, it penetrated rather deeply. As Gurdjieff was about to drive through the gates, he looked at me, saw the blood running down my leg, stopped, and asked me what had happened. I told him and he told me to wash it off, which I did as soon as he had left.

By the middle of the afternoon—he had left about noon— my leg was very painful, my knee swollen, and I had to stop work. The work I was assigned to that afternoon was cleaning the parquet floors of the salons, which meant scraping the floors with heavy steel wool to remove the old wax and accumulated dirt; this was done by standing on the steel wool and pushing it back and forth, with the grain of the wood, with one's foot.

By evening, my knee had swollen alarmingly, and I was not well enough to eat dinner. I was put to bed and various treatments began. Different people had different ideas about the treatments, but it was decided that the knee was badly infected and that the proper remedy was a hot onion poultice. Baked or perhaps boiled onions were placed on the open wound, which was then wrapped in heavy, transparent oiled cloth, and then wrapped again with a bandage. The purpose, of course, was to draw the poison out of the infected knee.

Although I received constant attention and the best of care— there was a resident doctor at the Prieuré who had supervised the treatments given me—my leg did not improve. By the following day it was enormous and small boils began to appear on my body, extending from well below my knee almost to my waist. I was delirious all day, coming out of my delirium occasionally when additional and more frequent poultices were applied. But nothing seemed to help.

It was late that afternoon when Gurdjieff returned from his trip. Some time after his arrival, when he inquired about me, he was told about my condition and he came to see me in my room. He removed the bandage and poultice and sent someone to the local pharmacy at once. They brought back a remedy, then called "Ouata-plasme", apparently also some form of poultice, and Gurdjieff had them build a fire in the stove in my room on which he could boil water. When the water was boiling, he dipped a small square of this impregnated cotton into the water, and then applied it immediately to the affected knee, again wrapping it in the oiled cloth and a bandage. He insisted that it be applied at once, directly from the boiling water, and I remember these applications as being excruciatingly painful. Instructions were given to someone to stay the night in my room and to apply these new poultices every four hours or so; which was done.

By the following afternoon, I was much better, and the poultices, when removed, were black with gelatinous, infected matter. That evening, Mr. Gurdjieff came to visit me again. As it was a Saturday and there was·to be a demonstration in the study-house, he insisted that I should attend along with all the others, and had his nephew carry me there and back "piggy-back". When we arrived at the study-house, he placed me in the small cubicle, where I sat behind him, during the demonstration. When it was over, I was carried back to my room. There was nothing very spectacular about the treatment or the cure, but Gurdjieff had something to say to me about it when I was on my feet again.

He asked to look at my leg, on which I was still wearing a small bandage, and when he had pronounced it cured, he asked me if I remembered what he had said about Philos helping me to identify his car when he arrived at the Prieuré gates. I said that I did, of course, and he said that these two things—the help of the dog, and the infection in my knee—had one thing in common. They were proof, of a kind, of man's dependence on other creatures. "To dog, you owe thanks, because he help you with small thing; to me you owe more than this, perhaps owe life to me. They try when I not here, even doctor try, fix your leg, but only get worse. When I come, I fix leg, because only I know about this new medicine which have in France now. I know this because I interested in everything, because necessary know all things for self in life. Just because I know this thing, and because I come back in time, you now well. You all right."

I said that I realized this and I thanked him for what he had done. He smiled, indulgently, and said that it was impossible to thank him for what he had done for me. "Cannot give thanks for life, not possible give enough thanks; also perhaps will be times when you wish I not save life. You young now, you glad not die—this serious thing, because illness like you have very dangerous, can even kill. But when you grow, you not always like life, and maybe you not thank me, but make curse on me because I not let die. So do not thank now."

He went on, then, to say that life was a "two-edged sword. In your country, you think life is only for pleasure. You have saying in your country: 'pursuit of happiness', and this saying show that people not understand life. Happiness is nothing, is only other side of unhappiness. But in your country, in most of world now, people only want happiness. Other things also important: suffering important because is also part of life, necessary part. Without suffering man cannot grow, but when you suffer, you think only of self, you feel sorry for self, wish not to suffer because this make you feel not comfortable, make you wish escape from thing that make you feel bad. When man suffer, he feel only self-pity. Not so if real man. Real man also sometimes feel happiness, real happiness; but when he also feel real suffering, he not try to stop this thing in self. He accept this because he know is proper to man. Must suffer to know truth about self; must learn suffer with will. When suffering come to man must make *intentional* suffering, must feel with all being; must wish with such suffering that it will help make conscious; help to understand.

"You have only physical suffering, suffering of body because of pain in leg. This suffering also help if you know how to use for self. But this is suffering like animal, not important suffering. With other suffering, suffering in all self, is possibility understand that all people suffer this way, is possibility also understand how depend on Nature, on other people, on everything, for help in life. Cannot live life alone. Aloneness—not loneliness, which is bad thing—but *aloneness* can be good thing for man, very necessary for life, but also necessary learn not live alone because real life depend on other human being and not just on self. Now, you still boy, cannot understand what I talk— but remember this thing; remember for time when you not thank me because I save life."

XXII

As that summer came to an end, many of the visiting Americans prepared to leave the Prieuré, probably never to see it again. They had been allowed to stay on even though the school had been reorganized, but it was not expected that they would be back the following year. It had again been decided, to my great relief, that we would not return to America that year, and I looked forward to the winter because Mr. Gurdjieff also was not planning to go away. Except for his occasional absences when it had been necessary for him to go to Paris on business, he had been in Fontainebleau constantly. His wife's condition, as he had predicted, was steadily worse all the time and we began to expect her imminent death.

In the several months that she had been confined to her room, I had only seen her once, when I had been sent to her room on some errand or other for Mr. Gurdjieff. The change in her had shocked and appalled me. She was incredibly thin, and although she did look at me with the semblance of a smile, even that small effort had seemed to exhaust her.

As the gardening and most of the outdoor projects came to an end for the winter, we began to make our usual preparations: drying fruit and vegetables, preparing meat for storage in large barrels in the cellars, cutting and splitting wood for all the stoves and fireplaces. Some of the floors of the school were closed off for the winter and some of the students even doubled up, sharing rooms to save on fuel. With the diminished number of students, most of our work was indoors as it had been the winter before; most of the available manpower was needed for general housekeeping and in the kitchens, stables, and the concierge.

The one event that loomed enticingly ahead of us, as the fall came to an end, was Christmas. It would be the first Christmas I had spent at the Prieuré when Mr. Gurdjieff was also there, and we had heard many stories about the elaborate Christmas ceremonies—there were always two celebrations, one for the "English" calendar and one for the "Russian" calendar which came two weeks later—and there would also be two New Years to celebrate as well as Gurdjieff's birthday which was, appropriately, on the first day of January by one or the other of these two calendars.

As the time approached, we began to make elaborate preparations. Various traditional holiday candies were made, cakes were baked and stored, and all the children were allowed to help in the preparation of what were called "guest presents", usually gaily coloured paper sacks of candies to be hung on the Christmas tree. The tree itself was huge. We cut it in the forest on the grounds of the Prieuré and it was set up in the main salon, so tall that it touched the very high ceiling. A day or so before Christmas, everyone helped with the trimming of the tree, which consisted mostly of hanging presents on the tree and also decorating it with hundreds of candles. A special, long pole was cut, to stand by the tree, to be used to put out any of the candles that threatened to set the tree on fire.

It was late on Christmas eve afternoon by the time that all the preparations had been made, and there was to be a feast that evening, after which everyone would join together in the salon for the distribution of presents, sometime that night. It was beginning to get dark when Mr. Gurdjieff sent for me. He talked to me about Christmas, asked me about previous Christmases in America and how I felt about that holiday, and when I had given him the expected answers, told me that, unfortunately, it was always necessary for some people to work on holidays in order that the others should be able to enjoy themselves. He mentioned the people who would be working in the kitchens, waiting on tables, cleaning up, and so forth, and then he said that someone would also, of course, have to be on duty at the concierge that evening. He was expecting a long distance telephone call and there would have to be someone there to answer it. He had chosen me because he knew that I could be trusted; also, I spoke English, French, and enough Russian to be able to deal with any telephone call that might come.

I was thunderstruck and could hardly believe what I was hearing. I could not remember ever having looked forward to any single celebration as I had looked forward to that one. He saw the disappointment in my face, of course, but said simply that while I would not be able to participate in the general festivities that night, I could look forward to Christmas that much longer, as I would get my presents on the following day. There was obviously no way in which I felt I could get out of this assigned duty, and I left him with a heavy heart. I had my supper early, in the kitchen, and then reported to relieve whoever had been assigned to the concierge that particular day. Normally, no one was on duty in the concierge at night. A Russian family lived on the upper floor of the building and answered the telephone or unlocked the gate on the few occasions when it might be necessary.

It had snowed the day before, and the front courtyard, between the concierge house and the main building, was covered with snow, glistening white, and lighted by the brilliant lamps in the long corridor and the main salon, both of which faced the courtyard. It was dark when I reported for duty, and I sat glumly, filled with self-pity, inside the small concierge house, staring at the lights of the big house. There was no activity there now, the rest of the students, at this time, would be about to go in to dinner.

It seemed an interminable time before I began to see people filing into the big salon. Someone began to light the candles on the tree, and I was unable to contain myself. I left the door to the concierge open, and approached as close to the main house as I could and still be reasonably certain that I would be able to hear the telephone if it should ring. It was very cold—also I was uncertain about just how far away I would be able to hear the telephone bell—and from time to time, as the tree was being lighted, I would run back to the concierge to warm myself and to stare angrily at the telephone. I was praying for it to ring, so that I would be able to join the others. All it did was to stare back at me, stern and silent.

When the distribution of the presents began, starting with the smallest children, I was unable to control myself, and, forgetting all my responsibilities, I went right up to the windows of the main salon. I had not been there more than a minute when Gurdjieff's eye caught me and he stood up and strode across the salon. I left the window and, as if he had sent for me, went directly to the entrance of the château instead of back to the concierge. He arrived at the door at almost the same time as I did, and we stood, momentarily, looking at each other through the glass door. Then he opened it with a sudden, harsh movement. "Why not at concierge? Why you here?" he demanded angrily.

I made some half-tearful protest about having to be on duty

when everyone else was celebrating Christmas, but he cut me short. "I tell you do this thing for me, and you not do. Impossible hear telephone from here, maybe ring now and you stand here and not hear. Go back." He had not raised his voice, but there was no question that he was very angry with me. I went back to the concierge, hurt and overflowing with self-pity, determined that I would not leave my post again, no matter what might happen.

It must have been close to midnight when the family who lived on the upper floor returned and I was allowed to leave for the night. I went back to my room, hating Gurdjieff, hating the Prieuré, and by this time almost feeling proud of my "sacrifice" for him. I vowed that I would never mention that evening to him or to anyone else; also, that Christmas would never mean anything to me again. I expected, however, that something would be done for me the following day, that Gurdjieff would explain it to me, or in some way "make it up to me". I still fancied myself as a sort of "favourite" because of my work in his rooms—my special position.

The following day, to my further chagrin, I was assigned to work in the kitchen, since they would need extra help; I would have enough time off to clean his rooms, and would be able to deliver coffee to him at any time he might want it. I saw him several times, briefly, during the day, but always with other people, and no reference was made to the previous evening. At some point during the afternoon, someone, who said they had been delegated by Gurdjieff, gave me some Christmas presents, small things plus a copy of Jules Verne's *Twenty Thousand Leagues Under the Sea*; and that was the end of Christmas, except for the interminable waiting on table that night at the Christmas dinner for all the students and various guests. Since I was, this time, not alone as a waiter, I was unable to feel that I had, once again, been singled out or "punished" as I felt I had been the night before.

While Gurdjieff never at any time made any reference to that evening, it did mark a change in my relationship with him. He no longer spoke to me as if I were a child, and my private "lessons" came to an end; nothing was said about this by Gurdjieff, and I felt too intimidated to bring up the question of the lessons. Even though there had been no telephone call of any kind on Christmas eve, I had a lurking suspicion that there might well have been one during one of the periods when

I had strayed away from the concierge house, and it preyed on my conscience. Even if there had not been a telephone call at all, I knew that I had "failed" in the duty that had been assigned to me, and I could not forget it for a long time.

XXIII

VERY EARLY ONE Spring morning, I awakened while it was still dark, with only the very faint light of the sun beginning to be visible on the horizon. Something troubled me that morning, but I could not imagine what it was; I had a vague feeling of restlessness, a sensation that something unusual was happening. In spite of my usual, lazy, comfortable habit of staying in bed until the very last moment—which was about six o'clock—I got up with the dawn and went down to the still-silent, cold kitchens. As much for my comfort as to help whoever was assigned to kitchen-boy duty that day, I began to build the fire in the big iron cook-stove, and while I was stoking it with coke, my buzzer rang (it rang simultaneously in my room and in the kitchen). It was early for Gurdjieff, but the ring fitted my sense of uneasiness, and I raced to his room. He was standing in the open doorway to the room, Philos at his side, and he looked at me urgently. "Go bring Dr. Schernvall right away," he commanded, and I turned to leave, but he stopped me, saying: "Madame Ostrovsky is dead. Better tell."

I raced out of the building, and ran to the house where Dr. Schernvall lived; a small house, not far from the chicken yard, which was named, probably by the French years before, "Paradou". Dr. and Mme. Schernvall, together with their young son, Nikolai, lived on the top floor of this building. The rest of the building housed Mr. Gurdjieff's brother, Dmitri, and his wife and four daughters. I awakened the Schernvalls and told them the news. Mme. Schernvall burst into tears, and the doctor began to dress hastily, and told me to go back and tell Mr. Gurdjieff that he was on his way.

When I got back to the main house, Mr. Gurdjieff was not in his room, so I went down the long hall to the opposite end of the building and knocked, timidly, on the door of Madame Ostrovsky's room. Mr. Gurdjieff came to the door, and I told him the doctor was on his way. He looked impassive, very tired, and very pale. He told me to wait near his room and tell the doctor where he was. The doctor appeared a few minutes later and I directed him to Mme. Ostrovsky's room. He had only been there a few minutes when Mr. Gurdjieff came out of the room. I was standing in the corridor, undecided, not knowing whether to wait for him or not. He looked at me without surprise and then asked me if I had the key to his room. I said that I did, and he said that I was not to come in and also that I was not to let anyone else in the room until he sent for me. Then, followed by Philos, he went down the long hall to his room, but did not allow Philos to go in with him. The dog, looking angrily at me, settled himself against the door as Mr. Gurdjieff locked it, and growled at me for the first time.

It was a long, sad day. We all performed our assigned tasks but a heavy cloud of sorrow hung over the school. It was one of the first real Spring days that year, and even the sunshine and the unaccustomed warmth of the day seemed inappropriate. All our work was done in a hushed silence; people spoke to each other in whispers, and an air of uncertainty spread through all the buildings. Presumably, the necessary arrangements for the funeral were being handled by someone, Dr. Schernvall, or Madame de Hartmann, but most of us were unaware of them. Everyone waited for Mr. Gurdjieff to appear, but there was no sign of life from his room, he had not had breakfast, did not ring for lunch or for dinner, or for coffee at any time during the entire day.

The following day, in the morning, Madame de Hartmann sent for me and said that she had knocked on Mr. Gurdjieff's door and had received no answer and asked me to give her my key. I said I could not give it to her and told her what Mr. Gurdjieff's instructions had been. She did not argue with me, but said that she was worried because they were going to move Madame Ostrovsky's body to the study-house where it would remain overnight until the funeral the following day; she thought that Mr. Gurdjieff should know about this, but in view of what he had told me she decided that she should not disturb him.

Late that afternoon, when there had still been no sign from Mr. Gurdjieff, I was sent for again. This time, Mme. de Hartmann said she would have to have the key. The Archbishop, presumably from the Greek Orthodox Church in Paris, had arrived, and Mr. Gurdjieff would have to be notified. After an inner struggle with myself, I finally gave in. The Archbishop's appearance was almost as forbidding as Gurdjieff's could be at times, and I could not stand up against his apparent importance.

A short while later, she found me again. She said that even with the key she was unable to get into the room. Philos would not let her come close enough to the door to get the key in the lock; that I would have to go, since Philos knew me well, and tell Mr. Gurdjieff that the Archbishop had arrived and must see him. Resigned and fearful of the consequences, I went up to his room. Philos looked at me without friendliness when I approached. I had tried to feed him the day before and also that morning, but he had refused to eat or even to drink water. Now, he watched me as I got the key out of my pocket, and seemed to decide that he would allow me to pass. He did not move, but as I opened the door he did allow me to step over him into the room.

Mr. Gurdjieff was sitting in a chair in his room—the first time I had ever seen him sitting in anything other than the bed—and looked at me without surprise. "Philos let you in?" he asked.

I nodded, and said that I was sorry to disturb him and that I had not forgotten his instructions but that the Archbishop had arrived and that Madame de Hartmann . . . He interrupted me with a wave of his hand. "Is all right," he said quietly, "must see Archbishop." Then he sighed, stood up, and said: "What day today?"

I told him that it was Saturday and he asked me if his brother, who was in charge of the fires at the Turkish bath, was preparing for the baths as usual. I said that I did not know, but that I would find out. He told me not to let him know, simply to tell Dmitri to have the baths ready as usual, and also to tell the cook that he would be down for dinner that night and that he wanted a very special meal to honour the Archbishop. Then he told me to feed Philos. I said that I had tried to feed him but that he had refused to eat. Gurdjieff smiled. "When I leave room, will eat. You feed again." Then he left the room, walking slowly and thoughtfully down the stairs.

This was my first experience with death and while Gurdjieff had changed—he seemed unusually pensive and extremely tired—more so than I had ever seen him—he did not fit my preconceived notions of grief. There were no manifestations of sorrow, no tears, just an unusual heaviness about him, as if it required great effort for him to move.

XXIV

THE TURKISH BATH consisted of three rooms, and a small furnace room in which Mr. Gurdjieff's brother, Dmitri, stoked the fires. The first room, into which one entered, was for dressing and undressing; the second room was a large, circular room, equipped with a shower and several water faucets, benches along all the walls, and a massage table in the centre of the room; the third room was the steam-room, with wooden benches on several levels.

In the first room there were two long rows of benches along one side of the room and opposite them a large, higher bench where Mr. Gurdjieff always sat, facing and looking down on the other men. Because of the number of men at the Prieuré the first summer I was there, Mr. Gurdjieff had told Tom and myself to climb up on his bench behind him, where we would sit, peering over his shoulders at the assembled company. Any "important" guests always sat directly in front of him. Now, even though the baths were no longer crowded since there were not as many students at the Prieuré since the reorganization of the school, Tom and I still occupied our places behind Mr. Gurdjieff; this had become a part of the ritual connected with the Saturday bathing.

Once we had all undressed, it was customary to spend about half an hour, most of the men smoking and talking, while Gurdjieff urged them to tell him stories; the stories, as at the swimming pool, were generally ribald or off-colour, at his insistence. Inevitably, before we proceeded to the steam-room, he would tell any newcomers a long, involved story about his exalted position as head of the Prieuré, and founder of the Institute, and the story always included references to Tom and myself as his "Cherubim" and "Seraphim".

Conventionally, because of my preconceptions about death, and since Mme. Ostrovsky had died only about thirty-six hours previously, I expected the ritual of the bath that particular Saturday night to be a mournful and lugubrious one. I could not have been more mistaken. When I arrived at the bath that evening, somewhat later than most of the others, I found

everyone still wearing their underwear and Mr. Gurdjieff and
the Archbishop were involved in a lengthy argument about the
problem of undressing. The Archbishop insisted that he could
not take a Turkish bath with no covering of any kind, and
refused to participate in the bath if the other men were to be
completely naked. The argument must have gone on for about
fifteen minutes after I arrived, and Gurdjieff seemed to be
enjoying it immensely. He made numerous references to the
Scriptures, and generally poked fun at the Archbishop's "false
modesty". The Archbishop remained adamant, and someone
was despatched back to the main house to find something we
could all wear. Apparently, the problem had come up before,
since the messenger returned with a large number of muslin
breech-cloths which had been unearthed somewhere. We were
all instructed to wear them, and to undress as modestly as
possible. When we finally went into the steam-room, feeling
uncomfortable and embarrassed in our unaccustomed attire,
Gurdjieff, as if he now had the Archbishop at his mercy,
gradually removed his breech-cloth, and one by one the
rest of us did the same. The Archbishop made no further
comments, but stubbornly kept his breech-cloth around his
waist.

When we left the steam-room and went into the middle room
to wash, Mr. Gurdjieff again directed a long harangue at the
Archbishop. He said that not only was this partial clothing
a form of false modesty but that it was psychologically and
physically harmful; that ancient civilizations were aware that
the most important cleansing rituals had to do with the so-
called "private parts" of the body, which could not be properly
cleaned if any garment was worn over them, and that, in fact,
many religious ceremonies in former civilizations had stressed
such cleanliness as a part of their religious and sacred rites.
The result was a compromise: the Archbishop did not object
to his arguments and agreed that we could do as we wished,
but that he would not, and he did not, remove his
covering.

After the bath, the argument continued in the first room,
the dressing-room, during the "cooling-off" period which also
lasted for about half an hour; Gurdjieff was determined about
not venturing into the night air after a steam bath. A cold
shower was essential, but cold air was forbidden. In the course
of the discussion in the dressing-room, Mr. Gurdjieff brought

up the question of funerals and said that one important measure of respect even for the dead was to attend their obsequies fully cleansed, in mind and body. His tone, which had been ribald in the beginning, serious in the washing room, had become conciliatory and persuasive and he reiterated that he had in no way intended to show disrespect to the Archbishop.

Whatever the differences between them, they apparently respected one another; at dinner, which was almost a banquet, the Archbishop turned out to be a convivial and well-mannered hard drinker, which pleased Mr. Gurdjieff, and they seemed to enjoy one another's company.

After dinner, although it was very late by that time, Mr. Gurdjieff had everyone assemble in the main salon and told us a long story about funeral customs in various civilizations. He said that since Mme. Ostrovsky wished it, she would have a proper funeral, as decreed by her Church, but he added that other customs which had existed in great civilizations in the distant past, civilizations that were literally unknown to modern man, were pertinent and important. He described one such funeral rite where it was the prevailing custom for all of the relatives and friends of the deceased to gather together for three days after the death of an individual. During this period they thought of, and told the assembled company, everything that had been considered an evil or harmful act—in short, a sin—that had been committed by the deceased during his or her lifetime; the purpose of this being to create opposition which would force the soul to fight its way out of the body of the deceased and make its way to another world.

During the funeral the following day, Mr. Gurdjieff remained silent and withdrawn from the rest of us, as if only his body were actually present among the mourners. He only intervened at one point in the ceremonies, at the moment when the body was to be removed from the study-house and placed on the hearse. At that moment, with the pall-bearers assembled, a woman who had been very close to his wife threw herself on the coffin, hysterically, literally wailing and sobbing with grief. Gurdjieff went over to her and removed her from the coffin, speaking to her quietly, and the funeral proceeded. We followed the coffin to the cemetery, on foot, and each one of us threw a small handful of earth on the coffin when it had been lowered into the open pit near the grave of his mother. After the services, Mr. Gurdjieff and all the rest of us paid our silent respects at the graves of his mother and of Katherine Mansfield, who was also buried there.

XXV

During the time of Mme. Ostrovsky's illness and Mr. Gurdjieff's daily sessions with her, one person, who had been a close friend of his wife for many years, seriously objected to what Mr. Gurdjieff was doing; her argument was that Mr. Gurdjieff was prolonging his wife's sufferings interminably and that this could not possibly serve any worthy or useful purpose—no matter what he had said about it. This woman was Mme. Schernvall, the doctor's wife, and her anger against Mr. Gurdjieff had reached such a pitch that, while she did continue to live at the Prieuré, she never appeared in his presence and refused to speak to him for several months. She would argue her case against him to anyone who happened to be within earshot, and even once told me a long story to illustrate his perfidy.

According to her, she and her husband, the doctor, were two of the original group who had come with Gurdjieff from Russia some years before. We had heard about the incredible difficulties they had encountered escaping the various forces involved in the Russian revolution and how they had finally made their way to Europe through Constantinople. One of the things which Madame Schernvall now brought up against Mr. Gurdjieff, as proof of his unreliability and even of his evil nature, was that it was largely thanks to her that they had finally been able to make their escape. Apparently, by the time they had reached Constantinople they were entirely out of funds and Mme. Schernvall made it possible for them to continue to Europe by lending a pair of very valuable earrings to Mr. Gurdjieff, which enabled them to hire a boat and cross the Black Sea. Even Madame Schernvall admitted, however, that she had not offered the earrings spontaneously. Mr. Gurdjieff had known of their existence and, as a last resort, had asked her for them, promising that he would leave them in Constantinople in good hands and that he would, on his honour, return them to her someday—as soon as he could raise the necessary money to redeem them. Several years had passed and, even though Mr. Gurdjieff had, in the meantime, raised large amounts of money in the United States, she had never seen the earrings again. Not only was this proof of his lack of good intentions; in addition she always brought up the question of what he had done with the money he had raised—had he not, for instance, purchased all those bicycles with money that could have been used to buy back her jewels?

This story had been told to most of us at different times, and at the time of Mme. Ostrovsky's death I had completely forgotten it. A few weeks after the funeral, Gurdjieff asked me one day if I had seen Mme. Schernvall recently and inquired as to her health. He expressed his regret at the fact that he never saw her any more and said that it made his relations with the doctor very difficult, and that it was not a good situation. He gave me a long lecture about the vagaries of women and said that he had finally decided that it was up to him to make an effort to win back Mme. Schernvall's affection and her goodwill. He then handed me part of a chocolate bar, in a torn box, as if someone had already eaten the other half, and told me to take it to her. I was to tell her how he felt about her, how much he did respect her and value her friendship, and to say that this chocolate was an expression of his esteem for her.

I looked at the torn wrapping and thought, privately, that this was hardly the way to win back her friendship, but I had learned not to express such reactions. I took it from him and went to see her.

Before handing her the small package, I gave her his messages, quoting him as exactly as I could, which took some time, and then handed her the little, torn package. She had listened to me with obviously mixed emotions and by the time I handed her the package she was eager to receive it. When she saw it, however, her features assumed a look of disdain. She said that he was never serious about anything, and that he had forced me to give her this long, elaborate message just as a preliminary joke to giving her a half-eaten piece of chocolate, which she did not like in any case.

I then said that I was surprised because he had told me that she liked this particular brand of chocolate above anything else in the world. She gave me an odd look when I said this and then opened the package hastily. He had chosen the right messenger; I had so completely forgotten her tale about the jewels that I was as astonished as she when she found, of course, the earrings. She burst into tears, hugged me, became almost hysterical; she made up her face, put on the earrings, and then proceeded to tell me the entire story all over again, but this time with the significant difference that this was proof of what a wonderful man he was, and how she had always known that he would keep his promise to her. I was as surprised by her switch of feelings as I had been when I saw the earrings.

I went back to him, as he had instructed me, and told him the whole story in detail. He was greatly amused by it, laughed a great deal, and then told me, at least in part, his story. He said that her facts were correct, but that she had no conception of the difficulties he had experienced in trying to get the earrings back. He had "pawned" them for a very large sum of money to a trusted friend in Constantinople and when he had, finally, been able to return the money, together with the proper interest, he had learned that his friend was dead. It had taken him, from then on, several years of unflagging effort to locate the jewels and to persuade the present owner, apparently a usurer, to return them for a sum far exceeding their value.

I could not help but blurt out my obvious reaction: Why had he done this? Were any jewels worth such a price, and, in addition, did Mme. Schernvall fail to realize that whatever the value of the jewels, the very lives of Gurdjieff's group at that time had probably depended on them?

He told me then that the value of the jewels was not an important element in the story. One reason he had redeemed them was because of his wife's friendship for Mme. Schernvall; that friendship could not be evaluated, and that it was necessary to do this for the sake of the memory of his wife. Further, he said that any man had an obligation to keep any promise that was made truthfully and solemnly, as he had made that particular promise. "I not do this for her only," he said, "also do for sake of my soul."

"You remember," he said then, "how I tell about good and evil in man—like right hand, left hand? In other sense, this also true of man and woman. Man is active, positive, good in Nature. Woman is passive, negative, evil. Not evil in your American sense like 'wrong', but very necessary evil; evil that make man good. Is like electric light—one wire passive or negative; other wire active, positive. Without such two elements not have light. If Mme. Schernvall not evil for me, perhaps I forget promise, serious promise, I make to her. So without her help, because she not let me forget what I promise, I not keep promise, not do good for own soul. When give back earrings I do good thing: good for me, for memory of wife, and good for Mme. Schernvall who now have great remorse in heart for bad things she say about me. This important lesson for you."

XXVI

Mr. Gurdjieff's relationship with me, although it continued in a surface sense to be the same, had undergone a definite change which I felt had begun with the previous Christmas. I continued to clean his rooms, bring him coffee, and do his errands, but the easy, affectionate feeling that had existed between us—almost like that of a father and son—seemed to be disappearing; it was as if he had set out to create a certain distance and reserve between us.

When he had talked to me before, whatever the subject of our conversations, he had often referred to the fact that I was still a child and that much of what he was saying was something that I could not, at the time, understand. But with the change, while he still talked to me frequently, his tone was more serious and he no longer referred to me as a boy. I felt that he was beginning to expect me to fend for myself, to use my own mind—that he was, in fact, urging me to grow up.

He often discussed human relations in general, the specific roles of male and female, and human destiny; as often as not these discussions were not directed to me exclusively, but to a group of which I was a member. He took pains to make it clear to us that whenever he addressed anyone on any subject in the hearing of others, it would or could be beneficial for everyone present to listen to what he was saying. Many of us had the feeling that when he addressed one individual he was often talking not so much to that person as to anyone in the group who might feel that the conversation was applicable to himself. We sometimes had the feeling that he was talking to a particular person through someone else; as if purposely not addressing one individual directly.

He came back to the theme of good and evil, active and passive, positive and negative, very frequently. I had been impressed with what he had said about Mme. Schernvall and himself in this regard when he had told me about the recovery of the earrings; it seemed to me to be a continuation of a theme on which he had spoken recurrently: the two-sided nature of man and the need to acquire or create a reconciling force.

This force, in an exterior sense, had to be created in human relations between individuals; in an "interior" sense, it had to be acquired or created within an individual as part of his own development and growth.

One of the most important things about Gurdjieff's pronouncements, talks, lectures, or discursions (everyone had his own name for them), was the enormous sway he had over his listeners. His gestures, his manner of expressing himself, the incredible range of tone and dynamics in his voice, and his use of emotion, all seemed calculated to spell-bind his auditors; perhaps to mesmerize them to such an extent that they were unable to argue with him at the time. Unquestionably, however many questions might come to a listener's mind when Gurdjieff had finished speaking, a deep and lasting impression had always been made before such questions arose. Not only did we not forget what he said to us, it was usually impossible to forget what he had said, even if one wished to forget it.

Shortly after the earring episode with Mme. Schernvall, he brought up once again the question of men and women, their roles in life, and, as an additional element, the specific roles of the sexes in his work or, for that matter, in any religious or psychological work which had self-development and proper growth as an aim. I was surprised and puzzled then, and many times later when he spoke on the subject, by his reiteration of the fact that not only was his work "not for everyone" but that "women did not need it." He said that the nature of women was such that "self development" in his sense of the phrase was something that they could not achieve. Among other things, he said: "Nature of woman is very different from that of man. Woman is from ground, and only hope for her to arise to another stage of development—to go to Heaven as you say—is *with* man. Woman already know everything, but such knowledge is of no use to her, in fact can almost be like poison to her, unless have man with her. Man have one thing that not exist in woman ever: what you call 'aspiration'. In life, man use this thing—this aspiration—for many things, all wrong for his life, but *must* use because have such need. Man—not woman—climb mountains, go under oceans, fly in air, because must do such thing. Impossible for him not to do; cannot resist this. Look at life around you: Man write music, man paint pictures, write books, all such things. Is way, he think, find Heaven for self."

When someone did object that the sciences and the arts were not, after all, exclusively confined to the world of the male, Gurdjieff laughed: "You ask question about woman artist, woman scientist. I tell you world all mixed up, and this true thing I say. True man and true woman not just one sex— not just male or female. True human is combination of these things: active and passive, male and female. Even you," he made a sweeping gesture covering all of us, "sometimes understand this because sometimes you surprised when you see man who feel thing like woman, or woman who act like man; or even when in self feel feelings proper to opposite sex.

"We all live in what we call universe, but this only very small solar system, smallest of many, many solar systems— even very unimportant place. For instance, in this solar system, people bi-sexual: necessary have two sexes for reproduction of kind—primitive method, which use part of man's aspiration for creation of more people. Man who can learn how to achieve higher self—how go to proper Heaven—can use all this aspiration for development of self, for what you call immortality. In world as now exist, no man able do this: only possibility for immortality is reproduction. When man have children, then all of him not die when his body die.

"Not necessary for woman do work of man in world. If woman can find real man, then woman become real woman without necessity work. But, like I tell, world mixed up. Today in world real man not exist, so woman even try to become man, do man's work which is wrong for her nature."

XXVII

Shortly after Madame Ostrovsky's death, the atmosphere at the Prieuré seemed to change; part of it was definitely due to her death (Gurdjieff, for example, was living with a woman who became pregnant a few months later); part of it was simply because I was, inevitably, growing up. Questions that had not occurred to me previously loomed in my mind. What was I doing in such a place, what was the purpose of the school, what sort of a man, after all, was Gurdjieff?

I suppose that early adolescence is a "normal" time in which a child begins to evaluate his surroundings, his parents, the people around him. It was easy enough for me to answer my questions concerning why I was there: the aimless, haphazard series of events that had led me there was fresh in my mind. But, by this time, the question of whether or not I wanted to be there became a different one. Up to that time I had had no control over the course my life had taken; nor had it occurred to me that I could have had any influence in determining that course. At thirteen, I still had no voice and no power over my "destiny" or my future, but I did have questions about them.

In the course of the comings and goings of all types of people at the Prieuré—visitors, semi-permanent residents—there were always discussions about Gurdjieff, about the purpose and/or value of his work. There were a great many "students" who left the Prieuré under more or less violent emotional circumstances: sometimes because Gurdjieff did not want them there, sometimes because of their own attitudes and feelings about him as a man.

During the two years that I had been there, I had been aware of, and had certainly subscribed to, the feeling and the belief that Gurdjieff could do no wrong; that whatever he did was purposeful, necessary, important, "right". I had not, up to then, needed to make any decisions about him on my own. But a time came when I began to look at him against my own background, with my own unconsciously acquired values, and to make some attempt to evaluate the man, the students, the school. A great number of questions, mostly unanswerable, arose.

What was the power of this man whose word was law, who knew more than anyone else, who held absolute sway over his "disciples"? There was no question in my mind about my personal relationship to him. I loved him, he had taken the place of my parents and he had unquestioned authority over me and devoted loyalty and affection from me. Even so, it was obvious that much of his effect on me, and his power over me, was due to the feelings of others—generally feelings of reverence and respect—and to my natural desire to conform. On the other hand, my personal feelings of awe and respect were less important than my fear of him. The fear had become unquestionably genuine the more I came to know him.

It had been impressive, enlightening and even amusing to watch him, at close range, when he reduced people to a pulp, as he had done in the case of Mr. Orage, in my presence. But was it not also significant that Mr. Orage had left the Prieuré shortly after that and had not returned? I had been told that he was teaching the Gurdjieff "work" in New York since that time, and it may have been that whatever Gurdjieff had done to Mr. Orage had been necessary; but, finally, who was to determine that?

Gurdjieff himself was no help. One of the unforgettable things he had said, and he had repeated it many times, was that what he called the "good" and "evil" in man grew together, equally; that man's potentiality to become either an "angel" or a "devil" was always equal. While he had spoken, frequently, of the necessity to create or acquire a "reconciling force" within oneself in order to deal with the "positive" and "negative" or "good" and "evil" sides of one's nature, he had also stated that the struggle, or "war", was never-ending; that the more one learned, the more difficult life would, inevitably, become. The prospect seemed to be one of "the more you learn the harder it will get." When he was countered, occasionally, with protests against this rather grim outlook on the future, he seemed invariably to answer with the more or less irrefutable statement that we—individually, or as a group—were unable to think clearly, were not sufficiently adult or grown-up to judge whether or not this was a proper and realistic future for man; whereas, *he knew* what he was talking about. I had no arguments with which I could defend the charge of incompetency against me; but I had no absolutely acceptable proof of his competence, either. His force, magnetism, power, ability, and even wisdom, were, perhaps, undeniable. But did the combination of these attributes, or qualities, create, automatically, the quality of competent judgment?

It is a waste of time to argue or to do battle with people who are convinced. The people who were interested in Gurdjieff always ended up in one of two categories: they were either for him or against him; they either stayed at the Prieuré, or continued to attend his "groups" in Paris, London, New York and elsewhere, because they were at least reasonably convinced that he had some kind of an answer; or else they left him and his "work" because they were convinced that he was a charlatan, or a devil, or—more simply—that he was wrong.

Given the goodwill of his auditors, he was incredibly convincing. His presence and his physical magnetism were undeniable and generally overwhelming. His logic—in practical ways—was impossible to refute, and never coloured or distorted by emotion; in that respect, in the purely *ordinary* problems of life, there was no question but that he played fair. He was a considerate and thoughtful judge in dealing with questions or disputes which arose in the course of running an establishment such as the Prieuré; it would have been ridiculous, and illogical, to argue with him or to call him unfair.

However, going back in my own mind at that age to such things as my various experiences with Miss Madison, what had he done to her? What was the effect on her when he rewarded all those who had defied her orders? Why had he put her in that position of authority? Of course, Miss Madison was physically present as an answer to those questions. She seemed to have become that much more a follower, that much more a devoted disciple, and apparently did not question what he had done to her. But was that, in the long run, any answer? Was it, perhaps, merely proof that Miss Madison was overpowered by his magnetism, his positive force?

I had the feeling then—and I have no valid reason to change that feeling or opinion almost forty years later—that he was perhaps searching for some individual or some force that could or would oppose him effectively. There were certainly no such opponents at the Prieuré. Even at that age, I began to have a certain contempt for the abject devotion of his adherents or "disciples". They spoke of him in hushed tones; when they did not understand a particular statement he had made, or something he had done, they blamed themselves, far too readily for my taste, for their lack of insight; in short, they worshipped him. The atmosphere that is created, somehow, by a group of people who "worship" an individual or a philosophy seemed then—and still seems now—to carry the seed of its own destruction with it; it certainly lends itself to ridicule. What was perplexing to me was Gurdjieff's own ridicule of his more convinced and devout followers (witness the case of the ladies and the "famous old wine"). In my childlike, simple way, I felt that he was likely to do anything at all—at the expense of anyone—for "fun"; to see what, if anything, was going to happen.

In my opinion he not only played games with his students, but the games were always "loaded" in his favour; he was playing against people he had called "sheep" to their faces; people who, in addition, accepted the term without protest. Among the devout there were a few who fenced with him verbally, but, in the long run, they seemed to be the ones who were the most "possessed" or "convinced"; daring to joke with him became proof of a certain intimacy with him—a privilege accorded to them because of their total agreement with his ideas—and in no sense an indication of rebellion. The rebellious did not stay at the Prieuré to exchange banter, and they were not permitted to stay to challenge or oppose him; the "philosophical dictatorship" brooked no opposition.

What began to obsess me, at thirteen, was a serious and, to me at least, a dangerous question. What was I dealing with? I did not mind the fact that he was perhaps making as much of a fool of me as he seemed to be making of others; I didn't know whether he was or not. But, if he was, I wanted to know why. I could not deny that it was amusing to me, as a child, to see Gurdjieff "expose" adults, to make fun of them, but did it serve any constructive purpose?

Even at that age I was somehow conscious that evil could, conceivably, produce good. When Gurdjieff would speak of "objective" morality and "subjective" morality, I was not left entirely in the dark. In the simplest sense it seemed to mean that custom governed subjective morality, whereas what Gurdjieff called "objective morality" was a matter of natural instinct and individual conscience. In discussing morality, he recommended living in accordance with the particular moral customs and habits of the society in which one lived—he was very fond of the phrase "When you live in Rome, live as the Romans do"—but he stressed the necessity of an individual, objective, personal "morality", based on conscience, rather than tradition, custom, or law. Marriage was a good example of a subjective moral custom; objectively, neither nature nor individual morality required such a sacrament.

I did not feel especially confused when I learned that the title of Gurdjieff's first book was "Beelzebub's Tales to His Grandson" or "An Impartial, Objective Criticism of Man". The idea that the devil—or Beelzebub—was the critic did not appal me. When Gurdjieff stated that Christ, Buddha, Mohammed, and other such prophets, were "messengers from the gods" who had, finally, *failed*, I could accept the implicit theory that perhaps it was time to give the devil his chance. I did not, as an adolescent, have such a good opinion of the world that I found it difficult to accept Gurdjieff's verdict that it was "all mixed up" or "upside down" or, in my own translation of his terms, a general mess. But if the mentioned prophets had, for some reason, "failed", was there any assurance, then, that Gurdjieff (or Beelzebub) was going to succeed?

Fail or succeed at what? I could accept the theory that there was something "wrong" with humanity, but I resisted the statement, on the part of an individual, that he knew exactly what was "wrong". Also, acceptance is not conviction, and in order to discuss seriously a cure it seemed to me logical that one would have to be convinced that the illness existed. Was I, then, going to be forced to form an opinion about the "condition of man"—to make a diagnosis? I was not equipped to do so, but I was not averse to making an attempt in that direction. The only answer that I could find was, of course, no answer at all.

All these speculations led back, inevitably, to Gurdjieff, the man. When he prescribed an exercise, such as "self-observation", with the avowed aim of getting to "know oneself", I had no argument with him and he had the weight of all organized religion behind him as he had pointed out. Perhaps the difference lay in the particular method, and I was in no position to judge the merits of his methods. The aim, however, was not a new one.

If I was to accept the premise that man is inferior to nature—and I was in no position to deny it—then I was immediately forced to consider the possibility that Gurdjieff, being a man, did not necessarily have all the answers—assuming that there are any. His philosophy, as I understood it at that age, was unquestionably attractive. Was it anything more than that? All "mystical" ideas are attractive to the inquisitive for the perfectly simple reason that they are mystical or, in some way, mysterious.

Such questions are troubling; they can threaten the self-confidence, the "raison-d'être", of a human being completely. My doubts and questions were like a nest of concentric circles—the very reason for life itself, for human existence, seemed to boil down to whether or not I could or would accept Gurdjieff as the man who held the key. The simple fact of living in his presence had made it impossible for me to retreat (which is not necessarily the proper word) into any "belief" or "faith" in any other existing religion or theory of life. I was attracted by his repudiation of organized activity—whether religious, philosophical, or even practical, I was further attracted by his seeming support of individual truth, or action. But what was terrifying was the inevitable concept of the uselessness of human life—individual or collective. The story of the acorns on the oak tree had impressed me as a child. The concept of human life as simply another form of organism—which might or might not develop—was new to me. But was Gurdjieff's work, actually, the proper means by which to grow into an "oak"? Was I, finally, dealing with the devil? Whoever he was, I liked him; I was certainly smitten with him. Even so, it remains significant that my only serious attempt at suicide occurred that year. I was tortured by the questions that did not cease to torment me—tortured to the point that I could not continue to ask them of myself, relentlessly, without finding some sort of answer. Obviously, to me, the only person who *might* have the answer was Gurdjieff himself, and since he was also, in all probability, the villain, I could not ask him directly. What I did was to drink a small bottle of wood alcohol. On the face of it, this was not a very determined effort, but I intended it seriously—the bottle was marked "Poison" and I believed it. The results of the attempt were not particularly dramatic. I became sick to my stomach, and did not even have to take an emetic.

The attempt was made at night, and when I saw Gurdjieff the following morning, when bringing him his customary coffee, he took one quick look at me and asked me what was wrong. I told him what I had done and also, rather shame-facedly, about my immediate physical reaction of sickness. At that moment I no longer cared whether he was the devil or not. His only comment was that in order to commit suicide successfully the effort had to be whole-hearted. He did not ask me why I had done it, and I remember having the curious sensation that as we faced each other that morning we were being completely, dispassionately honest with one another.

XXVIII

My questions and doubts about the Prieuré and Mr. Gurdjieff, obsessive as they had been for a short time, subsided rapidly. I was not concerned about this, but relieved to slip back into the day-to-day working routine, as if a great load had been removed from my shoulders.

The only obvious changes in the general life at the Prieuré after Madame Ostrovsky's death were that Gurdjieff began to take frequent trips for periods of several days or even as much as two weeks at a time; and that when he was in residence there were usually a great many more guests on weekends. When he would go on a trip, he would often take as many as five or six people with him, and almost everyone anticipated the possibility of being selected to accompany him. It became a kind of *cachet* to have been on a journey to Vichy or Évian or any of the popular resorts that he liked to visit. Gurdjieff's given reason for these trips was that he needed to travel and to see more people because of his writing, which he usually did now in cafés and restaurants, often sitting in the centre of a group of people, drinking coffee and writing interminably. Many of the people who went with him were actively engaged in the translation of his writings into various languages; in addition, he liked to travel with an entourage.

I saw less of him at this time, mostly because of his more frequent absences, but even when he was at the Prieuré I did not have as much private contact with him as I had had in the past. On the whole, I was glad of this, for although my questions had subsided in the sense that they were no longer at the forefront of my mind, my fear of him and a general lurking suspicion of his motives had at least partially replaced my personal and, up to then, rather complete devotion to him. I continued, however, to have either an accidental or perhaps in some way purposeful series of experiences with him.

One day when he was expected to return from one of his journeys, I was working in the kitchen, helping in the preparation of one of the usual, elaborate dinners which were always served on the days he returned. As I was moving a large kettle full of boiling water in order to stoke the fires, I somehow spilled it on myself, mainly on my entire right arm. I dropped the kettle, howling with pain, and Madame Schernvall, the cook of the day, screamed for help and sent someone for the doctor. Instead of the doctor, Gurdjieff appeared, completely unexpectedly, in the kitchen. He had arrived much earlier than we had anticipated. Without a word, and not even seeming to listen to Madame Schernvall's almost hysterical explanation of what had happened, he strode over to me, pulled me over to the stove, removed the iron rings and exposed the red-hot fire. He then seized my burned arm and held it, with all his force, over the open fire—probably not for more than a few seconds, although it seemed an eternity to me. When he released me, he said very seriously and calmly that the proper way to fight fire was with fire. "This way," he said, "you not have scar on arm. Burn already gone."

I was amazed and very much impressed—not only with the painful treatment, but also because of his completely unexpected appearance at just that moment. Inevitably, it did seem to be one of those fateful occurrences which I could not simply charge off to coincidence. Madame Schernvall told me, after he had left, that she had had a similar experience with him several years before, and knew that what he had done to me was the proper treatment for a burn, but that she would never have had the force or the courage to do it. We both remained overawed for the rest of the day and Madame Schernvall certainly encouraged my temptation to feel that his appearance at that time had been in some way supernatural. We continued to talk about it for several days, mostly because, as he had predicted, there was not only no scar, there was no pain and no physical evidence of any burn at all.

Gurdjieff's treatment of me from then on took a different form, and, in spite of the lack of private, personal contact with him, it did seem to me that he often singled me out for no obvious reasons.

A few weeks after the "burn cure" we were again preparing a large dinner as there were to be a great many guests that evening. The principal guest was the gendarme who had discovered Gurdjieff after his automobile accident a few summers before. When he arrived, he was installed in one of the sumptuous guest rooms on the same floor as Gurdjieff's room, and was then introduced to all of us. Gurdjieff praised him and told us how much he, and all of us, owed to this man. If it had not been for him, he, Gurdjieff, might easily be dead, and so on. The gendarme, in turn, told his version of the story; and he was greatly impressed with Gurdjieff as a person because of two specific things that had happened. The first was his discovery of Gurdjieff. He had been riding home at night, going off duty, when he had come upon the wrecked automobile, and had of course stopped to investigate the accident. The amazing thing about it was that, although seriously injured, Gurdjieff had somehow managed, apparently in a state of shock, to get out of the car, take a pillow and blanket from the car and lie down at the side of the road—the pillow under his head, and well covered with the blanket. Considering his injuries, the gendarme could not—to this day—bring himself to believe that Gurdjieff had done all this without assistance.

The second thing that had amazed him was that, although it had taken him almost two years after his recovery, Gurdjieff had managed to search him out, find him, and finally persuade him to come to the Prieuré as his guest for the weekend. There was, apparently, some reason for astonishment in this connection, although I never fully understood it; the records did not give the gendarme's name or something of the sort. Whatever it was, it had taken a great deal of effort and persistence in this case, and the gendarme was almost unable to accept the fact that someone had gone to that much trouble to thank him for what was, after all, only the normal performance of his duty.

The gendarme was seated at a place of honour at the table and Gurdjieff, as the meal began, poured the usual glasses of Armagnac for everyone (customarily, it was necessary—it was one of his rules—to drink a great number of toasts during a meal, and he always filled the glasses himself), including the gendarme. But the gendarme balked. His respect and friendship for Mr. Gurdjieff were boundless, as he said, but he was totally unable to drink such strong liquor—the most he ever drank was an occasional glass of wine.

Gurdjieff was always persistent when people objected to drinking these strong toasts with him, but in this case he was adamant. He argued, pleaded, even begged the gendarme to drink with him, and the gendarme categorically, and as politely as possible, refused. Finally, Gurdjieff said that the dinner could not proceed without the participation of the gendarme in these toasts, and, as if trying another tack with him, said that any man worth his salt had not only to be able to drink such toasts, but must actually drink them. He waved away the man's protests and said that he would show him that the liquor would not have any bad effects. "This not usual place," he said, meaning the Prieuré, "here is such good-will that anyone can drink without bad effects. Even children can drink here." To prove this point, he called me over to him—I was serving at the table that night.

When I was standing next to him, he poured a water glass full of Armagnac, and told me in Russian to drink it down at one gulp. I did, although I had never tasted such strong liquor before. When I had swallowed it, the tears came to my eyes, and my throat was burning, but I managed to get to the kitchen where the horrified cook told me to eat bread rapidly to ease my throat. The cook was his sister-in-law and was often highly critical of him. She told me firmly that only a mad man would force a child to drink "that stuff" and then sent me back to my duties as waiter. The liquor had such an immediate effect on me that, while I did continue to pass various dishes to the assembled guests, I only did so by staggering around the table and shoving the platters at them, feeling giddy and completely unconcerned. I had never exper-ienced such a sense of carefree well-being in my life. I thought it was particularly comical when Gurdjieff, each time I arrived near him, would direct attention to me and my complete sobriety. I remember having a strange feeling of separateness as if I had actually departed from the confines of my own body and was able to watch myself, as if from a distance, tottering gaily around the table with the heavy platters in my hands. I was especially pleased when the gendarme, apparently thanks to me, gave in and drank several toasts with Mr. Gurd-jieff and the other guests. I felt that it was all thanks to me and congratulated myself on some great, but not very well defined, accomplishment.

Even so, and in spite of my high spirits, the dinner seemed interminable, and I was greatly relieved when I was able to stagger off to my bed at a very late hour. It seemed to me that I had only been asleep for a few minutes when I heard the insistent ring of my buzzer. I was amazed to see that it was daylight, and managed to get into my clothes and answer the inevitable coffee summons. Gurdjieff laughed at me when I appeared in his room, and asked me how I felt. I said that I supposed that I was still drunk and described to him the way I had felt the night before. He nodded sagely, and told me that the liquor had produced a very interesting state in me, and that if I could achieve that kind of self-awareness when sober, it could be a very important accomplishment. Then he thanked me for my part in his experiment with the gendarme and added that he had picked me, especially, because it was very important that I should learn how to drink, and to learn at my age what the effects of liquor could be. "In future, when drunk," he said, "try to see self this same way as you saw last night. This can be very good exercise for you, will also help to not get drunk."

XXIX

LATE THAT SUMMER, Tom and I were chosen to be members of the party of five or six who were to accompany Mr. Gurdjieff on his next trip away from the Prieuré. We were among the first children to be selected for this honour and I looked forward to the day of our departure with anticipation and enthusiasm.

It was not until we were actually on the road that Gurdjieff informed us that our destination was Vichy, where he planned to stay for several days and write. Within the first hour or two, I learned quickly enough that travelling with Gurdjieff was not an ordinary experience. Although we were not, as far as I knew, in any hurry to reach our destination, he drove his car as if possessed. We would tear along the roads at a high rate of speed for a few hours, then he would stop abruptly to spend two or three hours at a café in a small town, where he would write incessantly; or we might stop somewhere in the country, along the side of the road, and unload great hampers of food and drink, blankets and pillows, and have a leisurely picnic after which everyone would take a nap.

Short of any actual mechanical breakdown, we seemed to have an unusual number of unnecessary experiences on the road. Someone—it might be me, or any one of the party— would be delegated to sit next to Gurdjieff with an open map with which to guide him. He would start off, having told the map reader which road he wished to take, and would then rapidly accelerate to top speed. The map reader's job was to watch the road signs and tell him when to turn off and otherwise give him directions. Invariably, he would manage to speed up before reaching any intersection, and almost equally invariably would fail to make a proper turn. Since he refused to go back, it was then necessary to guide him on whatever road we had happened on in the general direction of our destination. Inevitably, there would be long arguments, usually beginning with his cursing of whoever happened to be reading the map at the time, and finally joined in by everyone. There seemed to be a purpose in this, since it happened regularly no matter who was seated next to him as guide, and I could only ascribe it to his desire to keep everyone stirred up and alert.

Although we carried two spare wheels and tyres with us—one on each running board—we could have used several more. Even in those days, changing a wheel after a flat tyre was not a very complicated operation. With Gurdjieff, however, it seemed to become an engineering problem. When a tyre did go flat, and this happened often, everyone would descend from the car, different jobs would be assigned to the various members of the group—one would be in charge of the jack, another in charge of the removal of the spare tyre, another to remove the wheel that had to be changed. All of these jobs were then supervised by Gurdjieff personally, usually in conference with everyone who was not actually doing something. All work would stop from time to time and we would have long conferences about whether the jack would support the car at that particular angle on the road, which was the best way to remove the lugs from the wheel, and so on. Since Gurdjieff would never take time to have a tyre repaired at a gas station, once the two good spares had been used up, it became a question of not merely changing a wheel, but actually removing the tyre, repairing it, and replacing it on the wheel. On this particular trip, we had enough men to do this, but what with the arguments and conferences and a good deal of recrimination about why the tyres had not been repaired, this process took hours, and most of this time the entire group, with the women appropriately dressed in long dresses, would stand around the car in a huddle, advising and instructing. These groups of people gave passing motorists the impression that some great misfortune had overtaken us and they would frequently stop their cars to offer help, so that sometimes we would be joined by another large group which would also contribute advice, consolation, and sometimes even physical help.

In addition to the hazards of tyre repairs and finding ourselves almost constantly on the wrong road, there was no way that Gurdjieff could be induced to stop for gasoline. Whatever the gas gauge might read, he would insist that we could not possibly be out of gas until the inevitable moment when the motor would begin to cough and splutter and, although he would curse it loudly, the car would stop. Since he was rarely on the proper side of the road, it would then be necessary for everyone to get out of the car and push it to one side of the

road while some individual would be selected to either walk or
hitch-hike to the nearest gas station and bring back a mechanic.
Gurdjieff insisted on the mechanic because he was positive that
there was something wrong with the car; he could not have
done anything so simple as run out of gas. These delays were a
great annoyance to everyone except Mr. Gurdjieff who, once
someone had gone in search of help, would settle himself
comfortably at the side of the road, or perhaps remain in the
car, depending upon how he felt at the moment, and write
furiously in his notebooks, muttering to himself and licking the
point of one of his many pencils.

Gurdjieff also seemed to attract obstacles. If we were not
out of gas or on the wrong road, we would manage to run into
a herd of cows or a flock of sheep or goats. Gurdjieff would
follow such animals along the road, sometimes nudging them
with the bumper of the car, and always leaning out of the
driver's side hurling imprecations at them. We ran into a herd
of cattle during one of my tours of duty as map reader, and this
time, to my surprise and great pleasure, as he cursed at and
nudged one of the slower cows in the herd, the cow stopped
dead in front of the car, stared at him balefully, raised her tail
and showered the hood of the car with a stream of liquid
manure. Gurdjieff also seemed to think of this as being especially hilarious and we promptly stopped to rest at the side of
the road so that he could do some more writing while the rest
of us did what we could to clean up the automobile.

Another habit of Gurdjieff's which complicated these
voyages was that, having made numerous stops to eat, rest,
write, and so forth, during the day, he would never stop driving
at night until so late that most of the inns or hotels would be
closed by the time he decided that he needed to eat and sleep.
This always meant that one of the group—we all loathed this
duty—would have to get out of the car, and beat on the door
of some country inn until we could raise the proprietor, and,
frequently, the entire town. Presumably for the sole purpose of
creating additional confusion, once the owner of some inn or
hotel had been awakened, Gurdjieff would lean out from the
parked car, shouting instructions—usually in Russian—about
the number of rooms and meals that would be necessary and
any other instructions that might come to his mind. Then,
while his companions unloaded mountains of luggage, he would
usually engage in long, complicated excuses to whoever had

been awakened, deploring, in execrable French, the necessity of having awakened them and the inefficiency of his travelling companions, and so forth, with the result that the proprietress —it was nearly always a woman on such occasions—was completely charmed with him and would look at the rest of us with loathing as she served an excellent meal. The meal, of course, would go on interminably with long toasts to everyone present, especially the owners of the inn, plus additional toasts to the quality of the food, the magnificence of the location, or anything else that struck his fancy.

Although I thought the journey would never come to an end, we did manage to reach Vichy after a few days of this unusual manner of travelling. We did not arrive, of course, until very late at night, and again had to awaken a great many of the personnel at one of the big resort hotels, who, at first, informed us that they had no room. Gurdjieff intervened in these arrangements, however, and convinced the manager that his visit was of extreme importance. One of the reasons he gave was that he was the Headmaster of a very special school for wealthy Americans, and he produced Tom and myself, both very sleepy, as proof. With a perfectly straight face, I was introduced as Mr. Ford, the son of the famous Henry Ford, and Tom was introduced as Mr. Rockefeller, the son of the equally famous John D. Rockefeller. As I looked at the manager, I did not feel that he was swallowing this tale completely, but he managed (he was obviously tired, too) to smile and look at the two of us with deference. The one problem that remained to be settled was that there were not, in spite of Mr. Gurdjieff's possible importance, enough rooms for all of us. Gurdjieff considered this information seriously and finally devised some way in which we could all be accommodated without any improper mingling of the sexes, into the rooms that were available. Mr. Ford, or not, I ended up sleeping in his bathroom, in the bathtub. I had only just climbed into the tub, exhausted, with a blanket, when someone appeared with a cot that was squeezed into a narrow space in the bathroom. I then moved into the cot, whereupon Mr. Gurdjieff, greatly exhilarated by all these complications, proceeded to take a very hot and long-lasting bath.

The stay at Vichy was very peaceful as compared to our trip. We did not see Gurdjieff except at meals, and our only duty during our stay there was that we were under orders to drink certain specific waters which were, according to him, very beneficial. He gave orders about this water-drinking in the dining-room, which was full, much to our embarrassment and to the great enjoyment of the other guests in the hotel. The particular water that I was to drink was from a spring called "Pour les Femmes" and was a water whose properties were considered extremely beneficial for women, especially if they desired to become pregnant. Fortunately for me at the time—I was in an extremely good humour and enjoying the general spectacle he was making in the hotel—I thought that it was an extremely funny idea for me to drink waters which might induce pregnancy and enjoyed regaling him at meals with an account of the large number of glasses I had managed to drink since I had last seen him. He was very pleased with this and would pat my stomach reassuringly and then tell me how proud he was of me. He continued to refer to Tom and myself in a loud voice as Messrs. Rockefeller and Ford, and would explain to the maitre-d'hôtel, the waiters, or even the guests at nearby tables, about his school, and his remarkable pupils—indicating his young American millionaires-to-be—making learned remarks on the "real properties" of the waters of Vichy which were actually known only to himself.

To add to the general uproar of our stay at Vichy, Gurdjieff met a family of three Russians: a husband and wife and their daughter who must have been in her early twenties. He persuaded the hotel staff to rearrange the dining-room in order that this Russian family should be able to take their meals with us, and we became even more the centre of attraction of the hotel, what with the enormous quantities of Armagnac consumed at each meal, usually complete with toasts to all of the guests individually as well as to everyone at our table. It seems to me now that I only had time to eat tremendous, never-ending meals (I was not required to drink toasts, however), leave the table and race to the "Pour les Femmes" spring and consume large quantities of spring water and then rush back to the hotel in time for another meal.

The Russian family were very much taken with, and impressed by, Gurdjieff and after a day or so he had completely revised their water-drinking schedule, insisting that their régimes were completely wrong, so that the daughter ended up drinking, regularly, a water known, naturally, as "Pour les Hommes". She did not, however, find this particularly odd or funny, and listened very seriously to Mr. Gurdjieff's long, scientific analysis of the properties of this particular water and why it was the proper water for her to drink. When I asked him about this one night while he was taking a bath next to my cot in the bathroom, he said that—as he would prove to me sometime in the near future—this particular girl was very suitable for experiments in hypnosis.

We did not stay in Vichy for more than a week, and when we reached the Prieuré, late at night, after an equally harrowing return trip, we were all exhausted. Mr. Gurdjieff's only comment to me after the trip was that it had been a fine trip for all of us, and that it was an excellent way to "changer les idées".

XXX

SOMEWHAT TO THE surprise of all of us at the Prieuré, the Russian family that Gurdjieff had met in Vichy took him up on his invitation to visit the school. After welcoming them personally, he arranged for someone to entertain them during the afternoon, and then closeted himself in his room with his harmonium.

That evening, after another "feast", the guests were told to come to the main salon at a certain hour, and they retired to their rooms. During that time, he assembled all the rest of us in the salon and said that he wanted to explain, beforehand, an experiment which he was going to perform on the daughter. He reminded us that he had told us before that the daughter was "particularly hypnotizable" but he now added that she was one of the few people he had ever met who was susceptible to hypnotism of a special sort. He described the more or less popular form of hypnotism which usually consisted in requiring the subject to concentrate on an object before hypnotism could be induced.

He then said that there was a method of hypnotism, generally unknown in the western world, that was practised in the Orient. It could not be practised in the western world for a very good reason. It was hypnotism by the use of certain combinations of musical tones or chords, and it was almost impossible to find a subject that responded to the western or "half-tone" scale on, for example, an ordinary piano. The special susceptibility of the Russian girl who was visiting the Prieuré with her parents was that she was actually susceptible to combinations of half-tones, and it was this factor that was unusual about her. Given an instrument which could produce audible differentiations of, say, sixteenth-tones, he would be able to hypnotize, in this musical manner, any one of us.

He then had M. de Hartmann play, on the piano, a composition which he had written that very afternoon, especially for this occasion. The piece of music came to a kind of climax on a particular chord, and Gurdjieff said that when this chord was played in the presence of the Russian girl, she would immediately go into deep hypnosis, completely involuntary and unexpected on her part.

Gurdjieff always sat on a large, red couch at one end of the main salon, facing the entrance to the room, and when he saw that the Russian family was approaching, he indicated to M. de Hartmann that he was to begin to play, and then motioned to the guests to come in and seat themselves as the music was playing. He indicated a chair in the centre of the room for the daughter. She sat down in it, facing him and in full view of everyone in the room, and listened to the music intently, as if very moved by it. Sure enough, at the given predicted moment when the particular chord was played, she seemed to go completely limp and her head fell against the back of the chair.

As soon as M. de Hartmann finished, the alarmed parents rushed to the girl's side and Gurdjieff, standing by them, explained what he had done and also the fact of her very unusual susceptibility. The parents calmed down soon enough, but it took more than an hour to bring the girl back to consciousness, after which she was for perhaps two additional hours in a highly emotional, completely hysterical state, during which someone—designated by Gurdjieff—had to walk up and down on the terrace with her. Even after that, it was necessary for Gurdjieff to spend a large part of the night with her and her parents in order to persuade them to stay on at the Prieuré for several more days, and to convince them that he had not done her any irreparable harm.

He was apparently completely successful because they did agree to stay on, and the daughter even obliged him by submitting to the same experiment two or three times again. The results were always the same, although the period of hysteria after she returned to consciousness did not last for quite so long.

There was, of course, a great deal of talk as a result of these experiments. A good many people seemed to feel that there had been connivance on the part of the girl, and that there was no proof that she was not working with him. Even so, and without any medical knowledge, it was unquestionably true that she had been hypnotized, with or without her cooperation. Her trance was always complete, and no one could have feigned the manifestations of absolutely uncontrolled hysteria which always resulted.

The purpose of the experiments was something else again. They may have been conducted to dramatize the existence of a form of "science" which was unknown to us, but they also seemed, to some of us, just another demonstration of the way Gurdjieff would often "play" with people; they certainly stirred up another series of questions about Gurdjieff's work, his aims, and his purposes. The fact that the experiments seemed to prove a certain amount of unusual power and knowledge on his part was not, finally, necessary to most of us. Those of us who were at the Prieuré of our own choosing hardly needed such demonstrations to prove to us that Gurdjieff was, at least, unusual.

The experiments reawakened some of my questions about Gurdjieff, but more than anything else they produced a certain resistance in me. What I began to find difficult and irritating about just such things was that they tended to lead me into a realm in which I was lost. Much as I might have liked, at that age, to believe in "miracles" or to find reasons and answers concerning man's existence, I wanted some sort of tangible proof. Gurdjieff's own personal magnetism was often enough proof of his superior knowledge. He was generally credible to me because he was sufficiently "different" from other people—from anyone I had ever known—to be a convincing "super" man. On the other hand, I was troubled because I would always come up against a seemingly obvious fact: anyone who sets himself up as a teacher in any mystical or other-worldly sense had to be some sort of fanatic—totally convinced, totally devoted to a particular course, and, therefore, automatically opposed to the socially accepted, generally recognized, philosophies or religions. It was not only difficult to argue with him, there was nothing to argue against. One could, of course, argue about questions of method or technique but before that it was necessary to have agreed on some aim or purpose. I had no objection to his aim of "harmonious development" for mankind. There was nothing in the words that anyone could oppose.

It seemed to me that the only possible answer would have to lie in some sort of results: tangible, visible results in people— not in Gurdjieff—he was, as I have said, convincing enough. But what about his students? If they had been practising his method of harmonious development for several years, most of them, wouldn't it be somehow visible?

Except for Madame Ostrovsky, his deceased wife, I could think of no one other than Gurdjieff himself who had "commanded" any sort of respect by the simple fact of their presence.

One thing that a great many of the other, older students did have in common was what I thought of as a kind of "affected serenity". They managed to look composed and controlled or unruffled most of the time, but it was never quite believable. They gave an impression of being outwardly controlled that never rang quite true, particularly as it was easy enough for Gurdjieff to upset their equilibrium whenever he chose to do so, with the result that most of the senior students were always alternating between states of outward calm and hysteria. Their control seemed to me to be achieved by repression or suppression—I always felt that these words were synonyms—which I could not believe was desirable or worthwhile as an aim, other than socially. Gurdjieff frequently gave the impression of serenity, also, but it never seemed to be false in his case—generally speaking, he manifested whatever he happened to want to manifest at a particular time, and usually for a reason. One might well argue with the reason, and discuss his motives at length, but at least there was a reason—he appeared to know what he was doing and to have a direction; which was not so in the case of his students. Where his students seemed to attempt to rise above the ordinary tribulations of life by affecting a certain disregard for them, Gurdjieff at no time manifested calmness or "serenity" as if it were an aim in itself. He was far more likely to fly into a rage or to enjoy himself in an apparently uncontrolled fit of animal spirits than any of his students. On many occasions I heard him mock the seriousness of people, and remind them that it was essential for any well-rounded human being to "play". He used the word "play" and pointed out the example of nature—all animals knew, as humans did not, the value of "playing" every day. It seemed as simple as the trite "all work and no play makes Jack a dull boy"; no one could accuse Gurdjieff of not playing. By comparison his elder students were lugubrious and morose and were not very convincing examples of "harmonious development" which—if it was generally harmonious—would certainly include humour, laughter, etc., as at least aspects of well-rounded growth.

The women, particularly, were no help. The men, at least in the baths and at the swimming pool, did engage in earthy backyard human humour and seemed to enjoy themselves, but the women not only did not indulge in any humour, they even dressed the part of "disciples", wearing the kind of flowing clothing that is properly associated with people who become involved in "movements" of whatever kind. They gave the outer impression of being priestesses or novitiates in some religious order. None of it was either enlightening or convincing to a thirteen-year-old.

XXXI

THERE WERE TWO additions to the usual "winter" popula-
tion of the Prieuré after the exodus of the summer students in the
fall of 1927. One of them was a woman, whom I only remember
as being named Grace, and a new arrival, a young man by the
name of Serge. There was a certain amount of gossip about both
of them. In the case of Grace, who was the American wife of one
of the summer students—also American—she interested us
because she was not a new arrival but had stayed on after her
husband had gone back to America; also, because she was a
rather "unusual" student. None of us knew what she was doing
at the Prieuré, as she had never participated in any of the group
work projects, and was also exempt from such duties as working
in the kitchen or performing any household activities. And,
while no one questioned her status or her privileges, there was a
good deal of speculation about her.

Serge was a different matter. While I do not remember any
specific announcement from Gurdjieff about his arrival at the
Prieuré, we all knew, through the "student grapevine", that he
was on parole from a French prison; in fact, the gossip was that
his parole had been arranged by Gurdjieff personally as a
favour to an old friend. None of us had any exact information
about him; we did not know what his crime was (the children
all hoped it was something at least as lurid as murder) and he,
like Grace, was apparently also exempt from participation in
any regular functions at the school. We only saw these two
"students" (if that is what they were—we did not really know)
at meals and in the salon in the evenings. Grace, in addition,
used to make what we thought of as mysterious trips to Paris at
frequent intervals—mysterious only because, in the case of most
people, such trips were not only not frequent but their purpose
was usually known to all of us.

They both turned out to be very unusual additions to our
winter group. Late in the fall, when I was on concierge duty,
Grace was brought back to the Prieuré in the custody of two
gendarmes. She and the gendarmes had an interview with
Mr. Gurdjieff immediately after their arrival, and when the

gendarmes left, Grace retired to her room and did not even appear for dinner that evening. We did not see her again until some-time the next day, when she appeared once more at the con-cierge with all her bags packed and departed. We did not learn until a few days later that she had been picked up in a depart-ment store in Paris for shop-lifting and, according to the gossip (Gurdjieff never so much as mentioned her name), it had been necessary for Gurdjieff to guarantee her immediate departure from France back to America as well as to pay some large sum to the department store. The mystery of her isolated work at the Prieuré was also cleared up at that time. She had spent her time sewing, mostly making clothes for herself, with the materials she had been "lifting" in Paris. She was a topic of general conversa-tion for some time after her departure—it was the first contact that any of us had ever had with crime in the school.

Since Serge was known to be—or at least to have been—a criminal, our attention now focused on him. We had heard that he was the son of French-Russian parents, that he was in his early twenties, but other than that we knew nothing about him. He did not reward our interest by doing anything spectacular—for several weeks at least—until, just before Christmas, he simply disappeared.

His disappearance was first noticed when he failed to appear at the usual Saturday evening Turkish bath. That particular Saturday was somewhat unusual for winter-time because of the large number of guests that had come down from Paris for the weekend, among them several Americans who lived in Paris permanently. Although the fact of Serge's non-appearance at the bath was mentioned, no one was particularly concerned; we did not think of him as a full-fledged member of the group and he seemed to have a special status which had never been defined and which might, therefore, include such eccentricities.

As the next day was a Sunday—the one day when we did not have to get up and go to work at six o'clock in the morning—it was not until quite late, sometime before the customary "guest" lunch, that we learned that several of the Americans had lost money and jewels, or both, and that Serge had not reappeared. There was a great deal of talk about this at lunch and many of the guests inevitably concluded that the dis-appearance of their valuables and the disappearance of Serge were, of course, connected. Only Gurdjieff was adamant, main-taining that there was no connection at all. He insisted firmly, and, it seemed to most of us, unreasonably, that they had simply "misplaced" their money or jewellery, and that Serge would re-appear in due course. In spite of the arguments and talk about Serge and the "robberies" everyone managed to eat a big lunch and there was even more drinking than usual. By the time lunch was over and Gurdjieff was ready to retire for the afternoon, the Americans who had been, as they by this time insisted, robbed, could not talk of anything else and were con-sidering taking such measures as calling the police in spite of Gurdjieff's command that Serge was not to be implicated.

When Gurdjieff had retired to his room, it seemed natural enough for this group of Americans to sit together in one of the smaller salons and commiserate with one another as well as discuss whatever action they might take, and to drink during these discussions. Mostly because I spoke English and was also well known to all of them, they sent me to the kitchen for ice and glasses, having produced several bottles of liquor—mostly Cognac—from their rooms or their cars. For some reason or other, they began to insist that I should drink with them, and since I felt, as they did, that Gurdjieff was wrong about Serge, I was glad to join their group and even felt honoured to be in-vited to share their liquor. By mid-afternoon, I was drunk for the second time in my life, and enjoying it very much. Also, by that time, the liquor had fanned our feelings against Gurdjieff.

Our drinking bout was interrupted very late in the afternoon when someone came to get me, announcing at the same time that Gurdjieff was preparing to leave for Paris in a few minutes and that he wanted to see me. At first I refused to go with them, and did not go to the car to see him until he had sent a second person to get me. When I got to the car, followed this time by all my adult drinking companions, Gurdjieff looked at us all sternly, and then told me to go to his room and get a bottle of Nujol. He said that he had locked his door, and now could not find the key, and I had the only other existing key to his room.

I had my hands in my pockets at the time, and was feeling very courageous and also still angry with him. Although I was actually clenching the key in one hand I said, for no explicable reason, that I had also lost my key. Gurdjieff became very angry, began to shout at me, talking about my responsibilities and saying that losing his key was practically a crime, all of which only served to make me more determined. He ordered me to go and search my room and to find the key. Feeling very exuberant by then, and with the key still firmly in one hand in my pocket, I said I would gladly search my room but that I knew I would not find the key because I remembered losing it earlier in the day. Whereupon I went to my room, and actually made a search of the bureau drawers, and then returned to tell him that I could not find it anywhere.

Gurdjieff went into another tantrum, saying that the Nujol was very important—that Madame de Hartmann had to have it while she was in Paris. I said that she could buy some more at a drugstore. He said, furiously, that since there was already some in his room he was not going to buy any more and, further, that the drugstores were closed on Sundays. I said that even if there was some in his room, we could not get it without his key or my key, which were both lost, and that since even Fontainebleau had a "pharmacie de garde" open on Sundays, there must surely be a similar one in Paris.

All the spectators, particularly the Americans with whom I had been drinking all afternoon, seemed to find all this very amusing, particularly when Gurdjieff and Madame de Hartmann drove off, finally, in a rage without the Nujol.

I remember nothing further about that day except that I staggered to my own room and went to sleep. Sometime during the night I was very ill and the following morning I had my first experience with a real hangover, even though I didn't call it by that name at the time. When I appeared the next day, the Americans had departed and I was the centre of everyone's attention. I was warned that I would be severely punished and that I would most certainly lose my "status" as Gurdjieff's "caretaker". Sober, but with an aching head, I agreed and looked forward with horror to Gurdjieff's arrival that evening.

When he did arrive, I went to the car, like a lamb to slaughter. Gurdjieff did not say anything to me immediately and it was not until I had carried some of the luggage to his room and opened the door with my key and we were alone, that he held up his key, shook it at me, and said: "So, you find key?"

At first I said, simply, "Yes." But after a momentary silence I was unable to contain myself and added that I had never lost it. He asked me where it had been when he had wanted it the day before, and I told him that I had had it in my pocket all the time. He shook his head, looked at me incredulously, and then laughed. He said he would think about what he was going to do to me and would let me know later.

I did not have to wait for very long. It was just about dusk when he sent for me to come to see him on the terrace. I met him there and, without saying a word at first, he held out his hand. I looked at it and then looked up at his face inquiringly. "Give key," he said flatly.

I was holding the key in my hand in my pocket, as I had done the day before, and although I did not say anything, I did not hand it over, but simply looked at him, silent and imploring. He made a firm gesture with his hand, also without speaking, and I took the key out of my pocket, looked at it, and then handed it to him. He put it in his pocket, turned away from me and started to walk down one of the long paths, paralleling the lawns, in the direction of the Turkish bath. I stood in front of the terrace, watching his back fixedly, as if unable to move, for a very long time. I watched him until he had almost disappeared from sight and then I ran to the bicycle rack near the students' dining-room, jumped on my bicycle, and raced down the path after him. When I was within a few yards of him, he turned to look at me, I slowed down, got off my bicycle and went up to him.

We stared at each other silently for what seemed to me a very long time, and then he said, very quietly and seriously: "What you want?"

The tears came into my eyes and I held out my hand. "Please give me the key," I said.

He shook his head, very slowly, but very firmly. "No."

"I'll never do anything like that again," I pleaded. "Please."

He put his hand on my head, a very faint smile on his face. "Not important," he said. "I give you other work. But you now finished with key." He then took the two keys out of his pocket and held them up. "Have two keys now," he said, "you see, I also not lose key." Then he turned away from me to continue his walk.

XXXII

THE HABITS OF day to day living at the Prieuré occupied me to such an extent that I was very little concerned with my "family" life except for the letters I occasionally received from my mother from America. Also, although Jane and Margaret were permanently established in Paris, since Jane and I had reached a point of no communication, I rarely thought about them. I was brought back suddenly to the reality of my mother when, in early December of 1927, she wrote me that she was coming to Paris for Christmas. I was very pleased with this news, and promptly answered her letter.

To my amazement, only a few days later, Jane appeared at the Prieuré for the special purpose of discussing my mother's impending visit. I understood that, in view of her legal rights, it was necessary for her to give us permission to visit our mother in Paris and Jane had come to consider giving us this permission and also to consult Gurdjieff about it, and, doubtless, to find out how we felt about it.

Jane's argument that our serious work at the Prieuré would be interrupted by my mother's visit not only seemed to me absurd, but also brought all my questions to the fore again. I had been willing enough to accept the obvious fact that every-one connected with Gurdjieff and the Prieuré was "unusual"; the very word also meant that they were possibly special people—superior to or in some way better than people who were not involved with Gurdjieff. However, when I was con-fronted with this statement about serious work, I felt forced to make another attempt at evaluation. I had felt uncomfortable about my relationship with Jane for a long time, and it was un-questionably unusual for a legal guardian to visit a school and for her and her adopted son not to speak to one another for almost two years, but this did not, at first glance, seem superior. Since I had no ammunition with which to argue against the statements that I was either "impossible" or "difficult" or both, I had accepted this verdict on Jane's part; but after hearing her arguments about this impending visit I began to think again.

Since Jane's arguments only increased my stubborn determination that I was going to spend Christmas in Paris with Lois, Jane now insisted that not only did I have to have her permission but that I had to have Gurdjieff's permission too. All of this naturally led to a conference with Gurdjieff, although I realized later that only my continued insistence made that conference necessary.

We met solemnly in Gurdjieff's room and he listened, rather like a judge in a tribunal, to Jane's long account of her, and our, relations with my mother, and the importance of Gurdjieff and the Prieuré in our lives—what she wanted for us in the future, and so forth. Gurdjieff listened attentively to all of this, thought it over with a very serious look on his face, and then asked us if we had heard everything that Jane had said. We both said we had.

Then he asked, and even at that moment I thought it very adroit of him, if we realized how important it was "for Jane" that we stay at the Prieuré. Once more, we both said that we did, and Tom added that he also thought that any absence would "interrupt" his work.

Gurdjieff gave me a questioning look, but did not say anything. I said that except for the fact that I would not be available to do work in the kitchen or at some other task I did not think that my presence would be missed, and that, in addition, I was not aware of the importance of whatever it was I was supposed to be doing at the Prieuré. As he said nothing immediately in answer to this, I continued, adding that he had reminded me on many occasions that it was necessary to honour one's parents, and that I felt that I would in no sense be "honouring" my mother if I refused to see her; and that, in any case, I must owe her a good deal if only because, without her, I would not be alive to be anywhere—including the Prieuré.

Having listened to all of this, Gurdjieff then said that there was only one problem that had to be solved : it would be difficult for my mother if only one of us went to see her. He said that he wanted us to make our decisions honestly and individually, but that it would be better for everyone if we came to the same decision—either not to see her at all, or for both of us to visit her over Christmas.

After considerable discussion, in his presence, we arrived at a compromise which he accepted. We would both go to Paris to spend Christmas with Lois, but I would go for two weeks—the entire time she would be in Paris—and Tom would only go for one week, which would include Christmas but not New Year's. He said that he liked the holidays at the Prieuré and did not want to miss all of them. I said, promptly, that the holidays meant nothing to me; what was important to me was seeing Lois. To my great delight, Gurdjieff gave the necessary permission—two weeks for me, one week for Tom.

Although I was very happy to see my mother again, I did not consider Christmas or her visit an overwhelming success for anyone. I was very conscious of the opposite positions of Tom and myself—and inevitably reminded of the different decisions we had made some years before when it had been a question of spending Christmas with my father—and as long as Tom stayed in Paris, the fact that he was still determined to leave at the end of one week hung over all three of us like a cloud. And when he did return to the Prieuré after one week that cloud was replaced by the cloud of Lois' imminent departure. We talked a great deal about Jane and Gurdjieff, the fact of the adoption, and, perhaps for the first time since the year that we were adopted by Jane, the whole question became important again. For various reasons, most of which I no longer remember, it was evidently impossible for either of us to return to America at that time, but the very discussion of the question made me aware that, were it possible for me to leave France and return to America, I would certainly do so. My relationship with Jane— lack of relationship would have been more accurate, as I had not talked to her for almost two years except for the arguments about Christmas—was my main reason for wanting to leave. In every other way, and in spite of frequently being puzzled by Gurdjieff, I was content enough to be at the Prieuré. But at that time, with the entire question of why we were there, the emphasis upon the fact that Jane was our legal guardian, and the impossibility of being able to leave, all coming into strong focus at the same time, I began to resent everything and everyone, perhaps especially my own powerlessness. Lois was excluded from this resentment for the simple reason that she was, at that time, equally helpless and in no position to alter the situation.

Sad as I was when Lois left and I returned to the Prieuré, in another sense I was at least temporarily relieved of the pressure of all the questions that had come up. Nothing had changed, and I had to accept the situation, which turned out to be considerably less agonizing than worrying about it in futile attempts to find a way out of it. Even so, the resistances that had manifested themselves actively for the first time that Christmas did not vanish into thin air. I was determined that I would do everything I could to change the situation, even if I had to wait until I "grew up", which, quite unexpectedly then, no longer seemed to be in the distant, unforeseeable future.

XXXIII

My AWAKENING RESISTANCE to what I thought of as the "trap" I was in had little to do with Gurdjieff or the Prieuré itself. I was convinced that had I been a free agent (which, of course, at least implied adulthood) and had told Gurdjieff that I wanted to leave his school, he would have told me to leave at once. With the sole exception of Rachmilevitch, Gurdjieff had never asked—or tried to persuade—anyone to stay at the Prieuré. On the contrary, he sent a great many people away even when they would have given a great deal for the privilege of staying. Rachmilevitch's case was hardly in point, in any event, since he was paid to be there, according to Mr. Gurdjieff, and even he had only been "asked" to stay. For these reasons, I did not think of Mr. Gurdjieff as an obstacle.

The real obstacle, in my mind, was Jane; and since she was rarely at the Prieuré and then only for a day or two at a time, I tended to look upon Tom as her tangible representative. The experience of Christmas with my mother, and our different attitudes and feelings about it, had widened the existing gap of disagreement between Tom and myself. Either Gurdjieff or Jane had arranged for the two of us to share a room at the Prieuré that winter, and this new arrangement, of course, was not conducive to increased harmony.

During the years in which we had grown up together, Tom and I had both become accustomed to the use of different weapons. We were both impulsive and impatient, but we expressed ourselves in different ways. When we would quarrel with one another, our disagreements would always take the same form: Tom would lose his temper and would begin fighting—he had a great admiration for boxing and wrestling— and I would scorn fighting and confine myself to sarcasm and invective. Now, confined in the same room, it was as if we suddenly found ourselves in the strange position of having had our weapons changed for us. One night when he persisted in his general defence of Jane and his criticism of me, I at last managed to goad him into hitting out at me, and, for the first time in my life, once he had hit me—it was, I remember, important that he should strike the first blow—I hit him with all my strength and with the added force that seemed to have been building up inside me for some time. The blow was not only a hard one, it was completely unexpected, and Tom crashed to the tile floor of our bedroom. I was terrified when I heard his head hit the floor and then saw that he was bleeding—from the back of his head. He did not move immediately, but when he did get up and seemed to be, at least, alive, I took advantage of my superior position of the moment and told him that if he ever argued with me again I would kill him. My anger was genuine, and I meant—emotionally—what I was saying. The momentary fear I had experienced when he hit the floor had disappeared as soon as he had moved and I had felt immediately self-confident and very strong—as if I had liberated myself, once and for all, from physical fear.

We were separated a few days later and no longer lived in the same room, which I found a great relief. But even this was not the end of it. It had also, apparently, been brought to Mr. Gurdjieff's attention, and he spoke to me about it. He told me, seriously, that I was stronger than Tom—whether I knew it or not—and that the strong should not attack the weak; also that I should "honour my brother" in the same sense that I honoured my parents. Since I was, at that time, still sensitive about my mother's visit, and about Tom's, Jane's, and even Gurdjieff's attitudes about it, I answered angrily that I was not the one who needed advice about honouring anyone. He then said that the position was not the same—Tom was my older brother, which made a difference. I said that the fact of his being older did not make any difference to me. Gurdjieff then told me, angrily, that I should listen, for my own benefit, to what he was saying to me and that I was "sinning against my God" when I refused to listen. His anger only increased my own feeling of anger and I said that even if I was at his school, I did not think of him as my "God", and that whoever he was he was not necessarily always right about everything.

He looked at me coldly, and finally said quite calmly that I had misunderstood him if I thought that he was representing himself as a "God" of any sort—"you still sin against *your* God when you not listen to what I say"—and that since I would not listen to him, there was no point in talking to me any further about it.

XXXIV

THE ONLY PERMANENT job that was assigned to me that Spring was the care of a small, enclosed garden known as the Herb Garden. It was a small, shady triangular area near the irrigation ditch that ran through the property, and except for a certain amount of weeding, watering and hoeing there was not very much work to do there. The rest of the time I worked at the same old routine jobs and on various projects.

My jobs, however, were of less interest to me that Spring than some of the events and new arrivals. The first excitement of the year was the *dénouement* of the "Affaire Serge". We learned about it through one of the Americans who had suffered the greatest losses in what we had all come to think of as the "robbery". After the Americans had put the police on his trail, and several months after the actual robbery, he had been caught in Belgium, and although no valuables had been found on him, he had confessed the robbery to the police and some of the jewels had been found in the possession of an Arab "fence" in Paris. Serge had been brought back to France and imprisoned. Gurdjieff at no time made any comment on his failure to "rehabilitate" Serge, and the Americans who had been robbed generally thought that Gurdjieff was at fault for having allowed him to stay at the Prieuré in the first place. Gurdjieff did have some defenders among the older students, however, and their defence consisted in pointing out that jewels and money were unimportant—particularly to wealthy people—but that Serge's life did have value and that his imprisonment would probably ruin him for life, and that it was unfortunate that the police had been brought into the case. To a great many of us, however, this reasoning seemed to be nothing more than an attempt to maintain the position of Gurdjieff as never being wrong in anything he did—the common attitude of the "worshipful". Since Gurdjieff took no interest in the entire question, and since Serge was in prison, we lost our interest in the case soon enough.

For a short period in the late Spring I was again assigned to work on the lawns, not mowing them this time, but straightening and trimming the edges and borders. To my surprise, I was even given a helper, which made me feel like a dependable, experienced "old hand". I was even more surprised when I found that my helper was to be an American lady who, up to this time, had only made occasional weekend visits to the Prieuré. This time, as she told me, she was going to be there for two whole weeks, during which time she wanted to be a part of the "tremendously valuable experience" of working at what she called the "real thing".

She appeared for work the first day, looking very glamorous and colourful; she was wearing silk orange pants, with a green silk blouse, a string of pearls and high-heeled shoes. Although I was amused at the costume, I kept a perfectly straight face as I explained to her what she would have to do; I could not refrain from suggesting that her costume was not entirely appropriate, but I still did not smile. She waved away my suggestions as unimportant. She set to work, trimming the border of one of the lawns, with ardour, explaining to me that it was necessary to do this work with one's entire being and, of course, to observe oneself—the famous exercise of "self-observation"—in the process. She was using an odd sort of tool or implement which did not work very well: it was a kind of long-handled cutter, with a cutting wheel on one side and a small ordinary wheel on the other. The cutting wheel, of course, was supposed to actually cut the edge of the lawn in a straight line, while the other wheel helped to support and balance the apparatus and to give it power. The use of this implement required a good deal of strength to cut anything at all, since the blade was not very sharp; also, even when it was used by a strong man, it was then necessary to go over the edge that had been "trimmed" with this machine with a pair of long-handled garden shears and straighten up the border or edge.

I was so interested in her approach to this work and also in her manner of doing it that I did very little work myself, but watched her as she worked. She walked very gracefully, breathing in the country air, admiring the flowers, and, as she put it, "immersing herself in nature"; she also told me that she was "observing" her every movement as she worked and that she realized that one of the benefits of this exercise was that one could, through continuous practice, make every movement of one's body harmonious, functional, and therefore beautiful.

We worked together at this job for several days, and although

I finally had to actually trim all the edges and borders after her on my hands and knees with the long-handled shears, I enjoyed it very much. I had long since discarded the idea that work at the Prieuré was intended to produce the expected results (except of course in the kitchen) but that the work was done for the benefit of one's inner being or self. I had often found it very hard to concentrate on these invisible benefits, and much easier to simply, and unimaginatively, try to accomplish the visible, obvious, physical task. It was a pleasure to achieve a handsome, straight edge at the side of a lawn or flower bed. Not so with the lady, who when she realized, inevitably, that I was following her and doing all her work over again, made it clear to me that as long as our "selves" or our "inner beings" were benefiting from what we were doing it would not matter if it took us all year to finish the work—that, in fact, if we never finished it it would not matter.

I liked the lady well enough; I certainly enjoyed being her temporary "boss" and I had to admit that she looked handsome on the lawns, that even though she did not seem to accomplish anything that was visible, she was persistent and reported regularly for work. Also, for all I knew, she might have been doing a great deal of good work on her "inner being". I had to admit that she obviously made a point when she said that the actual results—on the land, as it were— were not very important. The grounds were living evidence of this—littered, as they were, with unfinished projects. All the work of uprooting trees and stumps, building new vegetable gardens, even the actual construction of buildings which remained unfinished, attested to the fact that physical results did not seem to matter.

I was sorry when our work on the lawns came to an end, and although I was dubious about the benefits she had, or had not, acquired in those few days, I had enjoyed my association with her. It gave me a somewhat different point of view about the school as a whole, and its purposes. While I had realized that none of the work was ever considered important from the simple point of view that it needed to be done; that there was, in short, another aim—the engendering of friction between people who worked together plus possible other, less tangible or visible results—I had also assumed that the actual accomplishment of the task itself had, at least, some value. Most of my jobs, up to that time, had supported this view:

it surely mattered, for instance, that the chickens and the other animals were fed and cared for, that the dishes and pots and pans in the kitchen were washed, that Gurdjieff's room was actually cleaned every day—with or without benefit to my "inner self".

Whatever thoughts I may have had about all of this and about her, the lady left after about two weeks, and seemed to feel herself "immeasurably enriched". Was it possible, after all, that she was right? If it had done nothing else, her visit had served to increase my need to re-examine the Prieuré and the reasons for its existence.

XXXV

My next temporary job on a project was the repair of the study-house roof. The construction of the roof was a simple affair of beams placed in such a way that they formed a peaked roof, with about eight feet of air-space at the centre between the peak of the roof and the ceiling. The beams were at intervals of about one yard—lengthwise and crosswise— and were covered with tar-paper which had begun to leak in various places. The job turned out to be exciting and rather perilous. We mounted the roof on ladders and from then on it was necessary to walk only on the beams, of course. It was also necessary to bring rolls of tar paper and pails or buckets of hot tar with us up the ladders. After a few days of walking on four- or six-inch beams we became reasonably proficient at this work and even made a sort of test of skills out of racing along the beams carrying a bucket of hot tar, or balancing a roll of tar paper on our shoulders.

One young American who was making his first visit to the Prieuré, and who was not only aggressive and very competitive but who also thought that everything at the Prieuré was, as he put it, "a bunch of nonsense", was determined to be more daring, more skilful and more foolhardy than anyone else. After about one week, he had manifested his superior agility to the point where none of us even attempted to compete with him. Even so, he seemed unable to stop showing off and continued to demonstrate his superiority over all the rest of us. His performance began to irritate all of us and to make us nervous; we did not go so far as to hope that he would have an accident—any accident could have been very serious as it was a high roof—but we did begin to long for something to happen that would bring an end to this exhibition of bravado.

The end did come, sooner than we had anticipated, and in a much more spectacular way. Later, it seemed inevitable that he would, of course, have been carrying a pail of boiling tar when he did make a false step on to the unsupported tar paper and fall through the roof. The only thing that saved him from very serious injury was that he had fallen just over the small balcony so that he did not actually fall more than about fifteen feet. However, what made the fall a brutal and painful one was that he did not let go of the bucket of tar and was not wearing a shirt at the time. One whole side of his body was very badly burned and covered with hot tar.

As the boiling tar had also flowed down inside his trousers, it was almost impossible for him to walk, so we moved him to a place in the shade while someone raced for Gurdjieff and the doctor. The only remedy—or, in any case, the remedy that was used—was to remove the tar from his body with gasoline, which took more than an hour, and which must have been almost unimaginably painful. The young man appeared to have tremendous endurance and courage, and submitted to this ordeal without flinching, but when it was over and he had been properly bandaged, Gurdjieff lashed into him in a great fury for his stupidity. He defended himself valiantly but without making much sense; the argument turned into a stream of invective against Gurdjieff and his ridiculous school, and ended with Gurdjieff ordering him to leave as soon as he was well enough.

While I could not help but feel great sympathy for the American, I did feel that Gurdjieff was completely right, although to revile the young man at that particular time had seemed unnecessarily cruel. I was very surprised when Gurdjieff, the following day, unexpectedly called to me when I was returning from work in the evening and, unpredictable as always, complimented me on my good work on the roof and gave me a large sum of money. I said that I had to admit, in all honesty, that since I was the only person working on the roof who was not a full-grown man, I had done considerably less work than anyone else and did not feel that I should be rewarded.

He gave me an odd smile, insisted that I take the money, and said that he was rewarding me for not having fallen through the roof or otherwise injured myself while I worked on it. He then said that he was giving me the money on the condition that I think of something to do with it for all the rest of the children—something that would be valuable for all of them. I left him, pleased with all the money I had in my pockets, but extremely puzzled as to what I could do with the money that would be valuable for all the other children.

After thinking about the problem for two days, I finally decided to share it with them, although not quite equally.

I kept a larger share for myself since I was the one who had, for whatever odd reasons, "earned" it.

Gurdjieff did not wait for me to tell him about what I had done, but sent for me and asked me, as if he was especially interested. When I told him, he was furious with me. He shouted at me, told me that I had not used my imagination, that I had not thought about it, and that I had not finally done anything valuable for them; also why had I kept a larger share for myself?

I said, calmly enough, that I had come to realize that nothing at the Prieuré was predictable and that he had made it clear to me often enough that things were never "what they seemed" to be. I maintained firmly that I had only emulated him. By giving me this totally unexpected large sum of money, he had, along with it, given me a condition and a problem concerning its disposition. Since I had been unable to think of anything "valuable" to do with the money, all I could do was to pass the problem along to the other children—my injunction to them being that they had to do something valuable with it for themselves. As to why I had kept a larger sum for myself, I said that I felt I deserved the larger sum because it was thanks to me that they had the opportunity to make this important decision about the value of money.

Although he had listened to me without interruption, his anger had not abated and he said that I was behaving like a "big-shot" and that he was extremely disappointed in me; that I had failed him.

To my own surprise, I stood my ground and said that if I was behaving like a "big-shot" it was because I had many examples of such behaviour to emulate, and that if he was disappointed in me he should remember that it was he who had told me, repeatedly, that one should learn never to be disappointed in anyone, and that, again, I was only following his advice and his example.

Although he told me then that I was, as usual, "sinning against my God" by talking to him in this way, he asked me what I was going to do with the money that I had kept for myself. I said that it was only possible either to spend money or to save it. That, for the time being, I was going to save it since I was clothed, fed and housed and did not need to spend it, but that I would spend it when I found something that I needed—or wanted—to buy.

He looked at me in disgust, remarking that what I had said indicated that I had typical middle-class morals and that I had not learned anything at all from him during the time that I had been at the Prieuré. I replied, rather hotly, that I was fully aware of those possibilities and that, as to learning, when I looked around me at his other students, I was not convinced that anyone else was learning anything either; that, in fact, I was not sure that there was anything to learn there.

Quite calm by this time, he said that I failed to realize that the value of the Prieuré was not necessarily obvious, and that time would tell whether anyone learned anything by being there. Then, for the second time, he said that it was useless to continue talking to me and added that I was not to continue my work on the roof of the study-house but that I would be assigned to other work.

XXXVI

My "OTHER WORK" consisted of several things: clearing various areas of the property of stinging nettles, which had to be done without wearing gloves; working, with one other person, on the construction of a stone house which had been partly built—and never worked on—ever since I had first been at the Prieuré; and, to my amazement, helping in the translation of parts of Gurdjieff's book from a preliminary French translation into English.

After a few hours on the job of pulling out nettles, I soon learned that with care, by pulling them out by the roots and avoiding handling the stems or leaves, it was possible to uproot them without being painfully stung by them. I also learned, quite incidentally, that they could be used to make an excellent soup. In any case, as I was still pondering about the American lady's remarks about the value of work, the uprooting of nettles did seem to have practical value as well as whatever it might have been doing for my "inner being", since it eliminated weeds and also provided soup.

As to the building of the house, I was convinced that the lady was undoubtedly right—no visible progress was made on the building so I assumed that all the progress was "spiritual". I was the helper on this job, and my "boss" decided that the first thing we were to do was to move an enormous pile of stone, located about fifty feet from the house, to an area next to it. The only sensible way to do this, he informed me, was for me to stand by the rock pile, throw individual rocks to him, and he would then throw them into a new pile near the building. When this was done, we would use the stones which had been moved to construct partitions or walls inside the building; the outer walls had been erected three or four years previously. I was warned that there was a definite rhythm to this rock throwing which had to be observed as it would make the work much less tiresome; also that in order to keep the proper rhythm it was necessary for us to sing. We only managed to sing and throw rocks for about two hours when my companion and "boss", distracted by something, failed to catch a rock that I had heaved in his direction, and was felled by it as it struck him on the temple.

I helped him to his feet and then walked with him as he more or less staggered in the direction of the main building, presumably to consult the doctor about the effect of this blow. Gurdjieff saw us at once as he was sitting in front of the terrace in one of his usual writing places, and when he heard what had happened, examined the man, pronounced him in no danger, but said that we were to discontinue working on that particular construction. With a rather amiable smile in my direction he told me that it was apparently impossible for me to be involved in any kind of work without causing trouble, and that I was a born troublemaker. Given some of my past experiences at the Prieuré I took this to be, if not exactly a compliment, at least praise of a kind.

I was fascinated, however, with the work on his book. An Englishman had been assigned to make a rough, preliminary translation from the French version of the book, and my job was to listen to it and read it and to make suggestions as to vernacular and Americanisms that would correspond as closely as possible to the French version which I was also to read. The particular chapter was on the subject of the continent of Africa and dealt mainly with Gurdjieff's explanation of the origin of monkeys.[1]

What began to interest me much more that summer than any of my daytime tasks were the nightly readings of the sections of Gurdjieff's book, usually in Russian or French but sometimes in English—depending upon the latest completed translations—and Gurdjieff's comments on his aims and purposes. In the simplest terms, he would usually reduce what had been written in the chapter that had been read that evening (his comments always followed the readings) to a kind of synopsis or simplification of what he was trying to convey in writing.

I was particularly impressed by his statement that his purpose in writing this book was to destroy forever the habitual values and ideas of people, which prevented them from understanding reality or living according to "cosmic laws". He was then going to write additional books which would prepare

[1] Gurdjieff, G. I., *All and Everything*; (Beelzebub's Tales to his Grandson; or an Impartial, Objective Criticism of Man). E. P. Dutton & Co., Inc., New York, N. Y.

the ground, as it were, for the acquisition of new understanding and new values. If, as I saw it, the existence of the Prieuré had the same aim: to destroy existing values, then it was more comprehensible. If, as Gurdjieff had so often said, the world was "upside down" then perhaps there was a definite value in what he was apparently attempting to do at his school. It might be quite true, as the American lady had suggested to me, that one should not work for the immediate, obvious result of the particular work one was doing, but for the development of one's being. Even though I was not convinced that Gurdjieff had all the answers to the dilemma of human life—as someone had called it—it was certainly possible that he, as well as anyone else, might have them. What he did do was at least provocative, unpredictable, irritating and, usually, interesting enough to arouse questions, doubts, and controversies.

In the course of his talks and comments on his writings, he frequently digressed from the subject of whatever had been read, to talk in general terms about almost anything that either came to his mind, or might be brought up by one of the students. When someone, through some association with the chapter that had been read that evening, brought up the question of the worlds of east and west, and the lack of understanding between the oriental and the occidental mentalities, Gurdjieff talked at some length on the misunderstandings that were created in the world by this lack of understanding, saying that it was due, at least in part, to lack of energy in the east and lack of wisdom in the west. He predicted that a day would come when the eastern world would again rise to a position of world importance and become a threat to the momentarily all-powerful, all-influential new culture of the western world, which was dominated, according to him, by America—a country that was very strong, to be sure, but also very young. He continued to say that one should look at the world in the same way that one looked at a man, or at oneself. Each individual was a world, of itself, and the globe—the big world in which we all lived—was, in a sense, only a reflection or an enlargement of the individual world in each one of us.

Among the purposes of all leaders, messiahs, messengers from the gods, and so forth, there was one fundamental and very important purpose: to find some means by which the two sides of man, and, therefore, the two sides of the earth, could live together in peace and harmony. He said that time was very short—it was necessary to achieve this harmony as soon as possible to avoid complete disaster. Philosophies, religions and other such movements had all failed to accomplish this aim, and the only possible way to accomplish it was through the individual development of man. As an individual developed his own, unknown potentialities, he would become strong and would, in turn, influence many more people. If enough individuals could develop themselves—even partially—into genuine, natural men, able to use the real potentialities that were proper to mankind, each such individual would then be able to convince and win over as many as a hundred other men, who would, each in his turn, upon achieving development, be able to influence another hundred, and so on.

He added, grimly, that he was in no sense joking when he had said that time was short. Further, he said that history had already proven to us that such tools as politics, religion, and any other organized movements which treated man "in the mass" and not as individual beings, were failures. That they would always be failures and that the separate, distinct growth of each individual in the world was the only possible solution.

Whether one believed him whole-heartedly or not, he made a convincing and passionate case for the importance of individual development and growth.

XXXVII

WHAT WITH ADOLESCENCE, lack of supervision, lack of interest, and just plain laziness, I managed to do as little work as possible in the Herb Garden. I avoided going there except when it was necessary for me to bring various herbs to the kitchen. When the quality of the herbs became noticeably poorer and when I was at times unable even to supply a small quantity of some particular herb, someone must have taken it upon themselves to investigate the garden and report their findings to Gurdjieff.

The result was that Gurdjieff made a personal inspection of the garden with me, walking up and down between all the small beds, examining every plant. When he had finished he told me that as far as he could see, I had done absolutely nothing at all there in the way of work. I had to admit that I had done very little work, but defended myself to the extent of pointing out that I had done some occasional weeding. He shook his head and said that in view of the state of the garden it would be better not to defend myself at all. He then assigned several of the children to work with me in the garden until it was in proper shape, and instructed me as to what had to be done to the various plants: hoeing between the rows, trimming certain plants, dividing and replanting others.

Although the children were very annoyed with me for having shirked my own work and thereby caused them to have to work on "my" garden, they all pitched in and we carried out Gurdjieff's orders very easily and quickly. It was a very small plot of land and it could not have taken us more than a day or two. When we had finished the work, Gurdjieff pronounced it satisfactory, complimented all the other children on their work, and said that he wanted to have a talk with me, alone.

He first told me that I could see for myself that I had not performed a task that had been assigned to me, and that it had been necessary for him to intervene in my work and take measures to repair the damage that had been caused by my neglect. He said that this was a very good example of the way in which one person's failure to accomplish his duty could affect the general welfare of everyone else and that, while I might not think of herbs as important, they were important to him and were needed in the kitchen; also that I had caused him an unnecessary, if minor, expense because various plants had had to be purchased, which would not have been necessary if I had done my job properly.

He went on to say that it was true, in one sense, that the herb garden was not important; what was important, however, was to be responsible and to do one's work, particularly when that work could affect the welfare of others. However, there was another, still more important reason for accomplishing any assigned task, which was for one's own sake.

He spoke again about the exercise of "self-observation" and said that since man was a three-centred or three-brained being, it was necessary to do exercises and perform tasks that were valuable for all three centres, not just the physical or "motor" centre; that "self-observation" as I knew it was a purely physical exercise in that it consisted in the observation of one's physical body and its movements, gestures and manifestations.

He said that there were various important exercises having to do with "self-remembering" which was a very important aspect of his work. One of them was to conscientiously and with all one's concentration, try to remember, as on a movie film, everything that one had done during each entire day. This was to be done every night before going to sleep. The most important thing in the exercise was not to let the attention wander—by association. If one's attention did wander from the focus upon the image of oneself, then it was absolutely necessary to begin all over again at the beginning each time this happened—and it would, he warned, happen.

He talked to me for a very long time that morning, and emphasized the fact that everyone had, usually, a particular, recurring problem in life. He said that these particular problems were usually a form of laziness, and that I was to think about my laziness, which took a fairly obvious physical form, as in the case of the garden: I had simply put off doing anything in the garden until someone had taken notice of that fact. He said that he wanted me to think seriously about my laziness—not the outward form, which was not important, but to find out what it was. "When you see that you are lazy, necessary find out what this laziness *is*. Because in some ways you already lazy for many years, can take even many years for you to find out what it is. Must ask yourself, whenever you see your own laziness: 'What is this laziness in me?' If you ask this question seriously, and with concentration, is possible someday you will find answer. This important and very difficult work I give you now."

I thanked him for what he had said and added that I was sorry that I had not done my work in the garden and that I would do it properly in the future.

He brushed aside my thanks and said that it was useless to be sorry. "Is too late for that now, and is also too late to do good work in garden. In life never have second chance, only have one chance. You had one time to do good work in garden, for self; you not do, so now even if you work all your life, in this garden, cannot be same thing for you. But also important not be 'sorry' about this; can waste all life feeling sorry. There is valuable thing sometimes, thing you call remorse. If man have real remorse for something he do that is not good, this can be valuable; but if only sorry and say will do same thing better in future is waste of time. This time is already gone forever, this part of your life is finished, you cannot live over again. Not important if you do good work in garden now, because will do for wrong reasons—to try to repair damage which cannot be repaired ever. This serious thing. But also very serious not to waste time feeling sorry or feeling regret, this only waste even more time. Must learn in life, not to make such mistakes, and must understand that once make mistake is made forever."

XXXVIII

IN THE COURSE of the readings of Gurdjieff's book, and particularly in his comments or talks which always followed them, he frequently discussed the subject of love. He pointed out that, in any attempt or effort to get to know oneself, it was always necessary to start with the physical body for the simple reason that it was the most highly developed of man's three centres; it was for this reason that "self-observation" always started by the observation of the body alone. While the body grew automatically and mechanically, practically without supervision, nevertheless it was a more properly developed centre than either the emotional or mental "brains" (or centres) because it did, even if only automatically, perform its proper functions. Most bodily functions were not only more or less compulsive, they were also reasonably comprehensible and therefore not too difficult to satisfy.

In relating the observation of the body to love, he again used the example of the two hands or arms, saying that love could be defined as "one hand washes the other". He also said that the body could achieve harmony within itself when it was used properly, when both hands worked together, and that this was a good place to start on the consciousness or awareness of what love really should be. In order for people to be able to work together, it was necessary for them to love each other, and to love the same aim. In this sense, in order for a human being to function properly and in accordance with his proper humanity, it was necessary for all of the component parts of a human being to love each other and to work together for the same aim—self-development and self-perfection; the difficulty was, of course, that given our abnormal habits and education we had no genuine conception of what proper development or "perfection " could be. He warned us against any misinterpretation of the word "perfection", stating that our associations with this word—our ideas of a "perfect" state—were improper, and that it was generally better to use the term "development".

The main indication or clue about love that we could learn

from the physical body was the physical form of love, in other words, sex. In the primary sense, the purpose of sex was reproduction, which was actually only a synonym for creation. Love, therefore, in any sense—whether physical or not—had to be creative. He also said that there was a proper form of what might be called "sublimation" of sexual energy; that sex was the source of all energy and when not used reproductively could still be used in an equally creative sense when sublimated and used as energy for other types of creativity. One of the misuses of sex that had arisen through bad training, the wrong type of education, and improper habits, was that it had become almost the only vital form of human communication. It was possible for people to "join actively" in other ways than physically; to, as he put it, "touch each other's essences", but human beings had lost this faculty many, many years—many centuries—ago. If one was observant, however, it was possible to realize that this "touching of essences" still occasionally took place between two individual human beings, but only by accident, and that it was then almost immediately misunderstood and misinterpreted and descended into a purely physical form which became valueless once it had been expended.

In talking further about relations between individuals, he said that sex, again, was the "highest expression of the physical body" and the only "holy" expression of self that was left to us. In order to achieve any other forms of "holiness" within ourselves, it was profitable to try—in other areas of our lives— to emulate this "essence-touching" process; and the completely open "sharing of common truth" between two individuals was almost always "visible" in a compulsive sexual relationship. He warned, however, that even sex—compulsive as it might be to most individuals—often dwindled into a simple process which only involved the particular satisfaction, gratification or release of a single individual, instead of both of them, and that in such cases there would not have been any openness or honesty between them.

When asked to define a proper, objectively moral love between people—one for another—he said that it would be necessary to develop oneself to such an extent that it would be possible to "know and understand enough to be able to aid someone else in doing something necessary for himself, even when that person was not conscious of the need, and might work against you"; that only in this sense was love properly responsible and worthy of the name of real love. He added that, even with the best of intentions, most people would be too afraid to love another person in an active sense, or even to attempt to do anything for them; and that one of the terrifying aspects of love was that while it was possible to help another person to a certain degree, it was not possible to actually "do" anything for them. "If see another man fall down, when he must walk, you can pick him up. But, although to take one more step is more necessary for him even than air, he must take this step alone; impossible for another person to take it for him."

XXXIX

IN SPEAKING OF his methods of self-development and proper growth, Gurdjieff would often emphasize the fact that there were many dangers that would inevitably be encountered in the process. One of the most frequent obstacles was that, at times, the performance of a particular exercise (he was referring to individual exercises prescribed by him for particular individuals) would produce a state of exhilaration or well-being. He said that while such a state of exhilaration was proper to the correct and serious performance of such exercises, one danger lay in our misconception of "results" or "progress"; it was necessary to remember that we should not expect results at all. If we did an exercise expecting a certain result, it was valueless. But, if we achieved a recognizable result, such as a feeling of genuine well-being, even though this was a proper, temporary, result, it did not in any sense mean that one had "achieved" anything permanent. It could mean that some progress was being made but it was then necessary to work that much harder in order to make such "results" a permanent part of oneself.

He referred, frequently, to a sort of riddle: a man, accompanied by three mutually hostile organisms, a lamb, a wolf, and a cabbage, arrives at the edge of a river which has to be crossed in a boat which can only carry two—the man and one other—"passengers" at a time. It is necessary to transport himself and his "companions" across the river without the possibility of one of them being able to attack or destroy the other. The important element in the story was that the general human tendency was to try to find a "short-cut", and the moral of the story was that there is no short-cut: that it is essential, always, to make the necessary number of trips to ensure the safety and well-being of all the passengers. He said that in the beginning, even though it would seem a waste of valuable time, it would frequently be necessary to make extra trips rather than to risk any possible danger. However, as one became accustomed to his exercises and methods, one should eventually be able to make only the exact number of trips required and still not endanger any passenger. It was also necessary to recognize the fact that in the case of the man, the lamb, the wolf and the cabbage it would be necessary to take some of the passengers on a return trip which would also seem a waste of time.

He used the same "riddle" as an example of the "centres" or "brains" of man; the man representing the "I" or the consciousness and the other three the physical, emotional, and mental centres. In addition to stressing the fact that the physical centre was the most developed of the three, he said that the mental centre was practically undeveloped, and that the emotional centre, which was partly developed—but in all the wrong ways—was completely "savage". He said that we responded to the needs of the body compulsively, which was proper as long as our bodily habits were good ones, since it was necessary to satisfy the needs of the body, or "machine", in the same sense that one would take proper care of a motor car since it was our only means of "transportation". With the emotional centre, since we knew almost nothing about it, the problem was much more difficult. Most of the errors of violence that were committed in the course of life were emotional, since we did not know how to use emotion properly in the course of our lives, and had only learned to form improper emotional habits from the moment we were born. He said that emotional "needs" existed that were just as compulsive as our physical needs such as hunger, sleep, sex, etc., but that we did not understand what they were and knew nothing at all about how to satisfy such emotional "cravings". One of the first steps was to understand that emotion was a kind of force within us. He frequently compared it to a balloon or to the reservoir of air that served to make a pipe-organ function. The pipes of the organ could be considered examples of various types of emotion, each pipe labelled differently: i.e., one pipe would be anger, another hate, another greed, another vanity, another jealousy, another pity, and so forth. One step towards the proper use of emotion was to be able to use the force or "air" in the reservoir in whichever of the pipes was proper or appropriate in a given situation, in much the same way as one consciously struck a certain note on an organ in order to produce a particular tone. If, for example, one felt—for whatever reason—anger, when anger was not appropriate to a particular circumstance or situation, instead of expressing anger, it should become possible for us to consciously divert that energy into whatever emotion was necessary or proper at the time. All existing emotions, all feelings, had purpose; there was a reason for their existence and a proper use for each one of them. But without consciousness or knowledge we used them blindly, compulsively and ignorantly, without any sort of control, producing the same effect in our emotional life as would have been produced, musically, by playing a pipe-organ as an animal might play it, without any knowledge, and without music—simply at random. The great danger of uncontrolled emotions was that "shock" generally produced effects in oneself and in others, and the force of shock was emotional. If from lack of consciousness or knowledge, one felt—mechanically—anger, instead of, for instance, compassion, at a time when compassion was the proper emotion, only havoc and chaos could be produced.

Most of the problems in communication and understanding between individuals resulted from just such emotional shocks which were inappropriate, unexpected, and therefore usually harmful and destructive. One of the subtler dangers involved in this was that people frequently tried to use a "shortcut" to the use of proper emotions. While feeling anger, they would attempt to control this feeling and express a different emotion—such as happiness, or love, or anything except anger. Since, whether we knew it or not, the simulated emotion did not convince other people emotionally, the result was that, in spite of the outward expression, the actual emotion or feeling would have been "recognized" as anger in any case, and having been sensed or felt in this way by another individual, in spite of not having been expressed honestly, it could be even more dangerous as it could only serve to arouse, although perhaps unconsciously, suspicion and hostility.

XL

IN SPITE OF my first beginning interest in the "theoretical" aspect of the Gurdjieff work at the Prieuré, this interest was cut short by two letters which I received shortly before Christmas in the year 1928. One was from Jane, who had arranged that Tom and I would spend Christmas with her in Paris, and I gathered that it was to be in the nature of a reconciliation between Jane and myself.

The second letter was from my mother in Chicago, who had been able to convince my stepfather that it was time for me to come back to the United States; there was even an enclosure from my stepfather asking me to come back and assuring me that I would be supported, educated, and welcome. My decision was instantaneous, and did not involve any inner conflicts. I wanted to return to America. Because my mother's letter indicated that Jane would not be either consulted or notified until they had heard from me, I decided not to mention the possibility of my leaving France until after Christmas.

We did go to Paris for Christmas, and Jane and I were reconciled. Since our relationship had always been characterized by its explosive quality, once we had, very emotionally, buried the past, I could not keep to my resolve, since I did not feel that I should disguise my intentions and wishes once we were on good terms again. I told Jane, honestly, and because of my new found goodwill towards her, that I wanted to return to the United States.

But I had forgotten that, as a minor, I could not leave Jane's custody, and that I should have to stay at the Prieuré, at least until I was of age.

It would be uninteresting and boring to even attempt to describe the nine months that followed. As far as any willing participation on my part was concerned, I might as well have left the Prieuré that very day. Although I continued to perform, in a desultory way, whatever work was assigned to me, my memory of that entire time is nothing more than a blur, punctuated only by letters from America and from Paris, visits by Jane to the Prieuré for the purpose of further argument, plus lectures and advice from many of the older students who had been brought into the argument by Jane, all of which, as was usual with me, only served to increase my determination to leave at any cost. I was particularly surprised, during the summer of that year, that Gurdjieff had not been brought actively into the question of my departure. He was finally brought into it in the early fall, presumably because of the influence and persistence of my mother and stepfather who had by this time even bought me a ticket, and had probably even gone so far—although I have no personal knowledge of this—as to threaten some sort of legal action. In any event, something had happened to cause Jane to consider agreeing to my departure. Her arguments now took the form of appeals to my good sense, rather than simple, straightforward threats.

Instead of seeing Gurdjieff at the Prieuré, I was taken to Paris to see him, in the company of Jane, at the Café de la Paix, which was his usual "writing café" when he was in Paris. We went there in the evening and Jane proceeded to talk for a very long time, advancing all of her arguments, deploring my resistance and the fact that I did not understand or realize that I was probably giving up the greatest opportunity for knowledge, and education, that I would ever have; she also went into the legal position at some length.

As always, Gurdjieff listened carefully and thoughtfully, but when she had finished he did not have very much to say. He asked me if I had listened to everything that she had said and if I had considered the whole situation. I said that I had and that my decision remained unchanged. He then told Jane that while he did not feel that there was much use for her to continue to argue with me about my decision, he would consider the whole situation and would talk to me, personally, in the near future.

When we had left him, Jane told me that, for me to leave at all, it would be necessary to break the adoption in so far as I was concerned—none of this related to Tom in any way—and that this could only be done through the American Consul in Paris; that it was very difficult and might even be impossible, and also that I was causing nothing but a great deal of trouble for everyone else in addition to giving up the opportunity of a lifetime. All I could do was listen and wonder if she would ever stop raging at me, and I took recourse in total silence.

Gurdjieff did talk to me, but only very briefly, when we were both back at the Prieuré. He said that he wanted to know if I had considered and evaluated my relationships to my mother, to Jane, and to himself and the school conscientiously and if, having done so, I still wanted to go back to America. I said that I thought I had, to the best of my ability, that I had been unhappy with Jane for several years now; as to himself and the Prieuré, I had no particular desire to leave the school or to part from him, but that I did want to be with my own family; that I was an American and would not, in any case, stay in France for the rest of my life. I felt that I belonged in America.

Gurdjieff did not object to any of this, and said that he would not oppose my leaving and that when Jane consulted him about it, he would tell her so.

The effect of Gurdjieff's decision not to oppose me was remarkable. Not only did Jane capitulate, but came to the Prieuré and announced that all the details—tickets, passport, legal papers, etc.—had been arranged. I was to leave in a few days and she, accompanied by Tom and a friend of hers, would drive me to Cherbourg to take the boat. I felt, instinctively, that this was an unnecessary journey and protested that I could just as well go on the train, but she was insistent about making the trip with me and putting me on the boat.

I said goodbye to Gurdjieff early in the afternoon of the same day that I was to leave. He was going to Paris and would not be there when we departed. The usual crowd was assembled at the entrance to the main building around his car, and he said goodbye to everyone. I hung back, feeling depressed and uncertain now that the moment was upon me, and he beckoned to me as he was about to get into his car. I went over to him, and first he shook my hand, looked at me with a smile on his face, and said, rather sadly I thought: "So you decide to go?"

I was only able to nod my head at him. Then he put his arm around me, leaned over and kissed my cheek, and said: "Must not be sad. Sometime maybe you will come back; remember that in life anything can happen."

At that moment, for the only time in many months, I regretted my decision. Whatever had taken place at the Prieuré, whatever I had or had not experienced or learned, my affection for Gurdjieff had remained essentially undi-

minished. I realized, although not immediately, that if he had
at any time put the question of my departure on a personal,
emotional level—the end of my personal association with
him—I probably would not have left. He did not; as I have
said, he always seemed to me to play fair.

EPILOGUE

XLI

W<small>HAT WAS THE</small> effect upon me of my years with Gurdjieff as a child, and what did I learn at the Prieuré?

I am tempted to answer that question with another question: How is it possible to evaluate such an experience? There was no training or education available at the Prieuré which would serve to prepare any individual for success in the ordinary sense of the word; I had not learned enough to enter a college, I could not even pass a final high school examination. I did not become a benevolent, wise, or even a more competent individual in any visible sense. I did not become a happier, more peaceful, or less troubled person. A few of the things I did learn—that life is lived today—right now—and that the fact of death is inevitable; that man is a perplexing, confusing and inexplicable, unimportant cog in the universe—are perhaps things that I might have learned anywhere.

However, I might well go back to the year 1924, and repeat that whatever else existence is or may seem to be, it is a gift. And like all gifts . . . anything is possible . . . there might be a miracle inside the box.

THE PENGUIN METAPHYSICAL LIBRARY

Some Other Volumes in This Series

THE SACRED PIPE: Black Elk's Account of the
  Seven Rites of the Oglala Sioux
Recorded and edited by Joseph Epes Brown

BORN IN TIBET
Chögyam Trungpa as told to Esmé Cramer Roberts

OUR LIFE WITH MR. GURDJIEFF
Thomas de Hartmann

ALCHEMY: Science of the Cosmos, Science of the Soul
Titus Burckhardt

STRANGE LIFE OF IVAN OSOKIN
P. D. Ouspensky

MY LIFE WITH A BRAHMIN FAMILY
Lizelle Reymond

THE NEW MAN: An Interpretation of Some Parables
  and Miracles of Christ
Maurice Nicoll

UNDERSTANDING ISLAM
Frithjof Schuon

HER-BAK, Volume 1: The Living Face of Ancient Egypt
Isha Schwaller de Lubicz

TO LIVE WITHIN
Lizelle Reymond

THE REIGN OF QUANTITY
René Guénon